Penguin Books
Pulsar 1

GW00642341

PULSAR 1

An Original Anthology of
Science Fiction and Science Futures
edited by George Hay

Penguin Books

Penguin Books Ltd, Harmondsworth,
Middlesex, England
Penguin Books, 625 Madison Avenue,
New York, New York 10022, U.S.A.
Penguin Books Australia Ltd, Ringwood,
Victoria, Australia
Penguin Books Canada Ltd, 2801 John Street,
Markham, Ontario, Canada L3R 1B4
Penguin Books (N.Z.) Ltd, 182–190 Wairau Road,
Auckland 10, New Zealand

First published 1978

Made and printed in Great Britain
by C. Nicholls & Company Ltd
Set in Monotype Times

For Mollie Gillam
With all of love

Contents

Introduction

George Hay

This introduction is not a lit. crit. thinkpiece: it is a statement of intent. *Pulsar* is intended to serve as a platform for those writers, scientists and humanists who are more concerned with what science fiction can *do* than with its literary pretensions. This sounds bitchy, but is not meant that way. Indeed, the Science Fiction Foundation, at the North East London Polytechnic, for which, as Belloc's verse has it, 'I fear that I am more or less to blame,' boasts what I believe to be the best academic journal on the subject in the English-speaking world, and possibly outside it – so I don't think I can be accused of knocking that particular establishment. However, I am very happy to be accused of knocking those, in or out of education, who are quite determined to shunt S F off into a literary siding where it can be relied upon, if not to die quietly, at least not to pollute the mandarins' tea-party.

I want to get the point across very firmly that the science fiction revolution, unlike so many others, is permanent. It can hardly help being so, since its main function is to dramatize the effects on society of new developments in scientific practice and thought. One of Sprague de Camp's characters remarked that people tended to be brought up to believe in eternal truths that were neither eternal nor true. It is so, but conservatives – of whatever political party – do not like to be reminded of this, since as they see it, their own security depends on being able to pass on to the young the idiocies for which they themselves have settled. Thus, anything genuinely revolutionary will be put down firmly, covertly for preference, and if need be, overtly – with blood on the pavement.

Perhaps you think I am exaggerating, just for effect? Well, read the passage that follows. It is by Philip K. Dick, and is strictly non-fiction:

9

Twenty-five years of devoted writing haven't in any way given me financial security . . . I am not quitting. It's going to take more than all this to make me give up science fiction writing, for one simple reason. I love to write it . . . It won't produce any financial security. The big break, just around the corner, will never come. One of these days I'll be back in the hospital, sick as hell, but I'll no doubt get out . . . and receive another $2,000 bill I have to pay off or go to jail. There are, in human beings, irrational drives. 'Why don't you get a *real* job?' people say to me, mostly in fun, but not always in fun, and sometimes I say it to myself . . . I guess there are eternal verities in the universe, all right, and the one which appeals to me is that man will keep on striving no matter how many times he is pushed down, which was what Faulkner said so thrillingly in his Nobel Prize speech. Man will be planning and scheming amid the ruins; the sound of his voice will still be heard.

I quote this from 'The Short Happy Life of a Science Fiction Writer', an article which appeared in an American fanzine, *Scintillation*. You should know, if you already don't, that most of the reliable data and general nitty-gritty on the genre comes, along with a lot of 'noise', from such periodicals as the American *Science Fiction Review*, and that that is where you should address yourself if you want to learn facts that may shock or enchant you, but which you will certainly not find elsewhere. For good critical material, try *Foundation, Extrapolation*, which serves the Science Fiction Research Association, or McGill University's *Science Fiction Studies*. For some facts – instead of the usual heated opinions – as to whether S F has or has not really helped mankind to head out to the stars, get hold of *The Spaceflight Revolution* by William Sims Bainbridge, published by Wiley Interscience. If you actually like talking and corresponding about the subject, you could join the British Science Fiction Association, which is looking up these days, and can put you in touch with a local group. The one thing *not* to do is to rely on the posh papers. Some of their reviewers are good and some not, but in any event, they just don't have the column space to cover the subject as it deserves. So it's back to the fanzines. I recall the first article by Stanislaw Lem I ever read, translated by Franz Rottensteiner in Vienna and sent over to Bruce Gillespie in Australia, for his 'zine and hence, back to Europe . . .

So you see, SF is quite a hot subject to stick around with. There's a lot of flak, and more support than one wants from the kind of friends whose presence eliminates the need for enemies. In recompense, one meets the kind of people also who are prepared, not just to think and talk about ideals, but to hang out and fight for them. Not all of these people are authors, or even strictly fans. Some of them are scientists, engineers – whatever. A few are famous, most are not, though possibly some of them should be. At all events, as I was saying, *Pulsar* is for them, as well as for the authors. As you'll see.

Frankly, this book is a risk. Maybe it is true that if all the average SF readers were laid end to end they would spell out, when seen from above, *Conan the Conqueror*. Maybe Penguin Books would have done better – if they could have got the rights – to have printed the eighty-seventh edition of *Gray Lensman* with a six-colour cover. Maybe readers really do not want to be reminded that they themselves are responsible for the exact location of that wavering boundary between fact and fiction.

And maybe not. Maybe – just maybe – there is a Silent Fringe awaiting the first step towards what Isaac Asimov has called 'the science fictionalization of the world'. In which case –

Be my guest.

Death Talk

A. E. van Vogt

The voice in his ear said, 'Olin Price, you are showing strong adrenaline reactions. Take note.'

Only seconds had gone by since Price had been savagely tossed out of the lind. So the feedback from the computer which monitored that condition was prompt.

He was plummeting rapidly. The air, though it was thin at this height, rushed past his headpiece with the beginning of a whistling sound. Since he, personally, was relieved at being away from where he had been mere moments ago, he was vaguely surprised that there was any reaction. Truth was, he felt calm. His thought: Better this attempt, however it ended, than even one more day of being under the control of Vrain.

He deduced that his body had its private responses. Which, of course, was the level at which the computer operated. Body reactions: muscular, chemical, neural, glandular.

'Fast heart beat, Olin Price,' said the small voice into his ear. 'Yet there is no indication of concomitant effort.'

And that – the swift pulse – seemed a little soon, also. From his vantage point he could see a misty planet below him. He guessed 20,000 metres still to go. Which meant that the instant of impact was many minutes away. It therefore should not be a factor in his immediate consideration.

I probably still have a decision to make.

Which was a pretty ridiculous idea, really. He was in a free fall without a parachute, and without any mechanical aids that were in his control.

So, essentially, all his decisions were already behind him. And, particularly, the final one that had motivated Vrain to throw him out.

13

All Vrain has to do is sit back and let me fall.

Moments after he had that thought, a different voice spoke through the tiny microphone inside his ear: 'Olin, I promise to leave your wife alone in future.'

It was Vrain's voice. The words were in the tone the officer used when he wanted to persuade someone.

Price said curtly, 'You promised that twice before, and broke your promise each time.'

'This time you've really convinced me,' was the reply. 'You never crossed me before to the point where I threw you overboard.'

Price said harshly, 'You're a man without morals, without any natural feelings of compassion. And right now you're a liar. So don't bother me.'

'Still' – the baritone voice remained conciliatory, un-offended – 'before you started calling me names, you did attach the sky dive cord. And left that in my control. So you hoped for something.'

In all his actions, that was the one thing Price had actually thought about, and hesitated. Yet in the end it had seemed to him that nothing else would be convincing.

Price spoke the only words he had rehearsed and in the exact bitter tone: 'My hope is that you'll be able to think of something that will solve the problem.'

'You have my promise.'

'That, General' – scathingly – 'is completely worthless.'

Pause. Then: 'Very well, Olin. Let me try to think of a satisfying foolproof system. And I'll get back to you.'

'You'd better make it quick,' said Price.

The scene below was a familiar one to Price. Living as he had in a lind, he had virtually all his adult life had a large view of the planet whenever he glanced out.

It had got to be pretty dull for the most part. The surface was so very far below, with no details really visible to the naked eye. Even the destroyed cities were merely more patterned blurs on the same mist-hidden, shadowed world.

Of course, there were the weekly sky diving competitions. Then the machos like Vrain would plunge down as Price was doing now. And the test of skill – and super-masculinity – was, who could fall the farthest before pulling out of his dive. Fortunately (if that were the right word) to control that required skilled technical types like Price. During a contest, he watched the divers closely. That could only be done through fine viewing instruments, which *did* show surface details.

Thus he had occasional reaffirmation of how barren, and, in its fashion, how beautiful the planet was. So empty. So desolate. So completely destroyed.

His thought was interrupted. 'If you'll look up,' said Vrain's voice, 'you'll see why you may suddenly acquire a renewed interest in saving yourself.'

Because he knew where to point his gaze, almost at once Price saw the tiny dot.

Again, Vrain's voice: 'As I see it, the best solution is for me to come down there and beat you up until you stop all this nonsense.'

As Price peered up at the moving dot, the other tiny voice said, 'Olin Price, you are experiencing an emotion akin to triumph – a special state of over-stimulation. Please observe that this is another extreme response.'

What Price was observing was that Vrain had attached a power flip to his legs. It was pushing him faster than would a natural fall. Still, there was time involved in catching up. And so Price, ignoring the computer, was able to say, scathingly, 'I should have guessed your solution would be he-man stuff.'

(That was a slight understatement. He had hoped, with total need for it to be so, that that would be the solution.)

Vrain was speaking: 'All I want to do is save your life. You can't be a hundred per cent opposed to that.'

Price replied, 'Don't you think it depends on what I'm being saved for? My home and family abused by a man who is incapable of true feeling about anything.'

That was as much interchange as there was time for. Abruptly, there was Vrain, his feet down now. The power flip slowed him until he was moving exactly as fast as Price.

It was a casually magnificent manoeuvre. For, as he came

out of his dive, he evidently stiffened by remote control the wire that supported him from the lind. The movement propelled him past Price in a long, graceful swing. Through the transparent helmet of the face part, Vrain grinned at Price as he whisked by. He waved an arm good-naturedly.

Vrain zoomed at least a quarter of a mile, like a man at the end of a swing. It was in its way an exact description. He was at the end of a fine, strong wire which supported him as the power flip could not: that is, it steadied him.

Having gone as far as it could, the officer's body started back towards him. As near as Price could make out, its direction was just about dead on. Inches only would separate them as they flashed by each other. Price sighed. And thought: 'Okay, baby, thank you for working it out for me.'

There was nothing to say, or, at least, that he ought to say. In coming down, as he had, Vrain had automatically put the wire support controls back on the board, and off of manual. And, quite simply, a technician understood that board and what was in it better than a sky diver.

No time to think about it. The body out there darted towards him like a bullet. Price waited until he literally saw the whites of Vrain's eyes through his headpiece.

What he did then, he touched a button on his own mechanic's suit that was not a part of an ordinary sky diver's equipment. Instantly, the machinery up there in the lind did its feedback balancing manoeuvre.

Vrain veered away, and passed at a distance of ten feet. Just before that final moment, he evidently saw that he was going to miss. His power flips came on. But all they could do was slow him. He must have had a thought, for he used the flips finally to hold him away from making another swing.

As they continued to fall together, Vrain said in an accusing tone, 'Did you do that? Or did I just miss?'

Decision. Moment of. That was the feeling. And it included the thought that a confrontation now ought to include a statement of total rebellion and hostility.

As if he realized his employee's (slave's?) dilemma, Vrain

said softly, 'Better think, Olin. There are 137 linds besides mine. Each has its technician like yourself, who is given special treatment and rights, including the right to marry. Each has an officer like me, capable, determined, in control of all the weapons through thought-monitored internalized computers. The officers comprise a defensive association, and stand by each other. The technicians are not allowed to inter-communicate one with another, and therefore have no opportunity to gang up on their employers. There are servants. These are not armed, but the males among them can exert physical force on behalf of the officers. Olin' – persuasively – 'it's a small group. But it's united, and smart, and determined, and cannot be defeated by one man.

'So, take my word. I sincerely regret what I have done. I swear that I shall leave Anais alone from now on. Let's get back there on the lind, and be on good terms again. I ask you, what else can you do that's sensible?'

It was the final appeal. Price recognized it as such. And there was no question: this was the moment of decision.

His altimeter showed 8370 metres, and the wind was a high squealing sound in his ears, as he fell and fell. What startled him, and held him silent, was the first, faint stirring of an impulse to agree with Vrain. To call it off. Impossible, of course, after all the things he had done earlier . . . that morning –

As he hesitated, the memory poured through him. Of his anger . . . It was his second time of checking personally to make sure Anais was in their quarters, and had not again been spirited upstairs to one of the fancy bedrooms.

. . . His decision (the solution of a weakling, as he thought of it now as he fell) to come up from his lind maintenance office every hour – What startled him as he glanced into the bedroom this second time, Anais was primping in front of her mirror.

For God's sake, that's what she was doing an hour ago!

Since she hadn't seen him, he was about to turn away. There *was* a small critical thought in him. The thought: What's the matter with women? The negative feeling modified rapidly into a tolerant acceptance that, really, there wasn't much even for

17

him to do in this isolated world of a lind in a fixed orbit above earth day after day.

He was in the act of gently closing the door, when the voice in his ear said, 'Olin Price, you have just experienced what for you is an unusual emotion. It correlates with suspicion. Take note.'

Price stopped: And mentally looked back at an incredibly miniscule thought he had had during that moment of feeling critical, and had instantly suppressed. In a manner of speaking, then, his inner eye stared at it in amazement.

Suspicion of Anais! What was stunning about it was that, now that it had been called to his attention, it made immediate sense . . . *She's excited by those three affairs with Vrain.*

It was a change from the dull existence of being cut off forever in this little apartment with a man who spent his spare moments reading old books.

(Many, many times he had argued with himself that access to the rescued books in Vrain's library all by itself justified his continued association with an S.O.B. But Anais didn't read; and she had long since exhausted the old films. So for her it had been listening to the same music, and sitting staring at the walls while she did so.)

Suddenly, her being in front of the mirror made a shattering impact on him: *She's trying to look enticing, so it'll happen again.*

By the time that thought/feeling tore part of his mind to tatters, he realized that he was inside the room. And that he must have made a sound; for she turned and glanced at him.

'Oh – it's you!'

He reached her in five long strides. He leaned past her towards the row of little bottles and jars on the vanity, and with a single thrust of his hand and arm brushed them.

The shove was so violent that even the least of the small objects zoomed ten feet. So forceful that a couple of items actually hit the wall twelve feet away at a higher height than where they had been.

'*Olin!*' It was a shocked cry.

Price snarled, 'No more make-up for you. No more pretty

dresses. No more doing your hair. And from now on you bathe only on the day that you and I make love.'

Moment later – the door slammed on her startled blue gaze. As he strode on, he realized he was imitating a smile of cold satisfaction he had seen many times on Vrain's face. And the small voice was saying: 'Olin Price, a brain stem signal indicates that for the last minute your thalamus and cortex have been disconnected by the process known as lower brain image takeover. Please observe, and consider the serious implications.'

'Yeah!' snarled Price defiantly. And refused to consider anything.

The images that were flooding up carried with them the seeds of schemes that in their time had been casual ideas, methods, plans. They were the stuff of rebellion against lind masters like Vrain. Nothing he had ever taken for real. Just a sharp, technical mind considering possibilities. After the first rape, the pictures were more violent, somehow. After the second one they carried a heavily charged feeling that someday somebody ought to do something.

And now –

He moved determinedly along a forbidden corridor, as if he had a right there. When he came to a barred door, he used a magnet key to unlock it. And pull it open.

The man who was inside must have heard the click. But he evidently did not at once realize that it was an unusual time for a visitor. He lay on the cot in one corner, facing away from the door. And it took half a minute before he turned and sat up.

'Olin!' he said then. 'For God's sake!' He must have seen the wildness in Price's eyes because he added, 'What's the matter, feller?'

Price said, 'Jim, if I put you back on the ground, what would you do?'

The thin face was gathering itself into something resembling its old identity. Suddenly, a faint smile. Then: 'Run!' said Jim.

'Where would you run to?'

More identity was returning. Memories showed in the eyes. Relevant thoughts. 'Why don't we say it like this, Olin. What do you want me to do down there?'

Silence. It seemed very definitely the moment of decision. Of coming to grips with the reality. Of accepting that, now, finally, he intended to confront Vrain, as he should have done after the first rape.

He said abruptly, 'Run into the forests. Get an army together. Signal me by a method I'll show you. Don't waste any time.'

There was total awareness, complete identity in the human object that had been in this . . . dungeon . . . for nearly a year. Jim said, 'Once down there, how do you know I'll do what you want? I will – but how can I prove it?'

'You,' said Olin Price, grimly, 'will have some micro-stuff put in your body. And then, if you don't keep your promise, you'll regret it.'

Within an hour, King Jim of the grounders was plummeting towards the distant earth at the end of a dive cord. He would release himself on making contact. Thereupon, he would run into the forest. The cord would dangle. Wait for his return.

Still, the driven feeling was inside Price. He took the elevator up. Up to the spread-out living quarters where Vrain and his five women dwelt. Moments later, moving along a corridor past one room filled with antique French furniture, past another open door through which he glimpsed the stunning beauty of the grand Italian furnishings, and came to a third door – closed – and stopped.

A servant was coming along the hallway. It was a man Price knew, who evidently accepted that the technician was upstairs for a reason; for he nodded as he went by.

Price couldn't remember who this particular individual was; but each servant aboard a lind was selected from among the helpless grounders far below. Held up here in 138 linds, they represented families of the survivors. Hostages in the oldest meaning of the term – guarantors of good behaviour, and guarantors for regular food delivery.

In return – they were given the privilege of having their best-looking women kidnapped into 138 harems. Once again, as was historically true, there was no mercy in the men who had the power. Alleviations, yes. Smiles, of course (of power, of triumph). Tenderness, once initial resistance was over-come... But don't cross me – if you do, I bite.

Were they good guys, in any way, these lind masters? Pro-bably – within the frame of male dominance ... Move outside that frame, and I kill –

Since they gave no mercy, none need be offered them.

'Olin Pirice,' said the tiny voice, 'you have believed that computer feedback awareness of body reactions could have saved civilzation had it been widely available. Yet you your-self are now letting personal emotion override such aware-ness. Too much adrenaline, great sugar depletion, rapid iodine utilization, vitamin C used up, wide-ranging internal dys-function, rapid ageing – the strongest emotions a combination of anger and anguish. Take heed.'

Price had the door open, and was inside Vrain's study. This was where the books were, and he had been given permission to come here, and borrow what he wished. But this was not book day, or hour, or minute. Price headed for the special private instrument board in one corner of the room, behind a large library desk. It was here, by touching certain buttons, that lind masters communicated with each other.

The small voice said, 'Olin Price, the formless images from the lower brain continue to dominate.'

... Push this button, turn that dial, pick up the receiver. As he listened, a firm, baritone voice said, 'General Dansky here.'

Price gulped, 'Hospadeen General Dansky, this is Olin Price, technician for General Vrain. May I speak to you?'

Having uttered the fateful words, Price had his first, vague, conscious thought. He had done the final dangerous prelimi-nary, and, in effect, stepped over the edge of the abyss.

'Olin Price,' said the small voice, 'there has been a great rush of blood to your stomach. The presumption is that you are in a startle/fear response. Take note.'

Price had no time for taking note. Because another implanted chip-size computer was giving a translation of Hospadeen (which it interpreted as 'Mr') Dansky's reply: 'Perhaps' – grimly – 'I should hear your reason for illegally addressing me.'

It was as much acceptance as he could hope for. And the fear faded. At once the stopped feeling was gone. His voice was steady as he said, 'General Dansky, I intend to kill General Vrain today. I believe that when I have done so, I may need help. What are the chances of you hearing me out and then of helping me?'

The reply was in the same grim tone: 'I'm willing to hear you out because your plan may affect all lind masters. Keep talking.'

Like everyone else, Price had early in his life accepted that people were lucky to get away from the ground. He remembered his father's desperate ambition for him. The older man, a physicist, had taught him all the lind theory and practice. And, fact, once he had understanding of Lind (*l*aser *i*nduced *n*egative *d*egravitation), it wasn't long before the grapevine channelled him to a location where the linds procured their ground supplies. After that it was up and away. Later, on his request to Vrain, he was allowed to come down and look for a wife. Of the several hundred girls he'd met in his week of wandering, every single one waited anxiously for his decision. It was the primitive ground life versus the reputed luxury universe of the linds. There were no hold-backs. And so he had got the prettiest girl of all: Anais.

But, also – during that week – he had met Kosorov, General Dansky's technician. What made the chance meeting important, Kosorov, an older man, had realized what an incredible coincidence it was. Kosorov had a plan, and a method – a contact system for the two of them, which he had forced a then reluctant Price to listen to. His argument: 'Look, my friend, the contact potential will just be there, and I'll be there, waiting – in case you ever want to take advantage. And, what's really decisive, Dansky absolutely hates the Americans like Vrain. Considers them responsible for the planetary disaster, which destroyed Dansky's whole family. Don't ever' –

Kosorov urged – 'underestimate the power of that kind of hatred.' Afterwards, it had occurred to Price that the hatred of Technician Kosorov for General Dansky was also a timeless condition, not to be underestimated.

... Thus, the illegal conversation from Vrain's study between a technician, Price (now that he wanted to 'take advantage'), and a lind master, Dansky, was not impossible at all.

– The battle, since it was phoney on Price's side, wove back and forth across a vast sky. Vrain, with his power flips to aid him, would, one moment, be a dot in the distance. Then – the darting attack.

Each time, by a cunningly planned, narrowing margin, Price achieved a miss. But progressively Vrain came closer. And faster. And oftener. Several times, as he flashed by, the officer stretched towards him and, with his thin, hard, metal rod, tried to strike at him.

With each miss, Vrain got angrier. 'By God' – his voice came, furious ' – if you don't stop your fall, I'm going to burn you.'

That was flinch stuff. For this was the power of the lind masters. These middle-aged men – actually, their ages ranged from Vrain's forty-one to (it was reported) several sixty-year-olds – had inside their bodies (implanted before the disaster) the micro-computers that controlled, and directed the weaponry of the linds. A technician of a particular lind could, for safety reasons, to prevent accidental discharges, interpose a delaying relay.

It was a twenty-second delay. Long enough for the technician to transmit a questioning signal to the lind master – meaning: 'Did you intend to do this, or did you not?' After that, all control was in he who controlled the computers.

At slightly over 4000 metres it was still a sky universe. But the ground below looked darker and no longer mist-hidden. And there was no doubt: the battle was descending to its hard climax.

The small voice said, 'Olin Price, you show a marked blood sugar depletion. A glass of orange juice, perhaps.'

‒ *Where is General Dansky?* ... Each time after Vrain darted by, Price tilted back, and sent his gaze up into the vault of the sky above, searching, seeking, hoping.

He said he would do it. Was it just a ploy? Could Kosorov have been wrong?

The thought ceased. Because ‒ a black dot. Far above, it moved against a fleecy cloud. Price allowed himself only an anxious moment or two to track it ‒ and then, there was Vrain again. As usual, the officer, a skilful sky fighter, was dead on his target.

Okay, thought Price, *this time we meet.*

He had often wondered what it was like when two metal and unbreakable plastic suits with 200-pound macho males inside crashed into each other. Now he would find out the smashing way.

It wasn't that simple. Price took no evasive action, but at the penultimate moment the swooping Vrain seemed to realize.

His flips came on. And even then he was too close to use his rod as a weapon. After he was past, when it was already too late, he struck with it. Came back with flip power, struck again.

Price let it happen ‒ leaving himself only one protection.

A line that is dangling from a point 17,000 or more metres away transmits its tugging energy at a finite speed. Predicting how slow that would be, Price had set the automatic control to move him three feet in randomly selected directions every ten seconds. It was these impulses, programmed in advance, that tugged the wire, and moved him sometimes out of Vrain's way and sometimes not. During those first minutes Vrain lunged six times, and Price's luck was not bad. Four misses and two hard blows from the rod.

They were really hard. The suit material transmitted the shock almost like a direct hit from a blunt instrument. The first hit was on his left arm, below the elbow. The second numbed his right thigh.

There never was a third hit. For within instants after lunge number six, Vrain seemed to pause. And then his strained voice came on their intercom: 'Olin, I have just received a message from General Dansky that you called him, and he's here to help you kill me because he hates my guts.'

Price was bobbing back and forth, and so he saw Dansky as an unevenly moving object a few hundred feet away. 'Okay,' he thought, 'this is it! Kosorov's plan.'

There was no time to consider anything else. Just do and say the plan.

He did it and he said it. And the first act was to signal Kosorov. And the second was the set speech to Vrain on their intercom: 'Sir, our private quarrel is suspended. In an emergency I am a loyal technician. Burn him!'

And that worked because Kosorov, waiting for and perceiving the signal in the distant lind of his master, triggered the delaying relay on Dansky's weapon control system.

The doomed Russian plunged down toward the dark world below. Smoke and flame poured from his dead body and from his burning suit. *Vrain, next!*

On the way up, back to the lind, the officer was grim. 'There will have to be an interrogation, Olin. However, your evident change of heart, your earlier emotional disturbance, and your action of supporting me in a crisis, and of course the outcome, will limit the penalty to some lashes.'

Price said, 'What about some lashes for you for rape?' But he didn't say the words aloud. For the fate of Vrain and others like him had been predetermined by a dictum of Kosorov. His was a capital offence. He had taken total advantage of a post-world-destruction situation to help create a total tyranny. And yet –

Later.

. . . And yet, it seemed wrong, somehow, to see Vrain lying there dead. They had lowered the second corpse to the ground; and Price had followed. But it was not an easy thing to accept, mentally.

They gave Vrain a funeral, and put him in a rough box. Price walked by with the others, and when it was his turn he stopped and looked down at the still face. What the others had thought was not obvious. But Price's feeling was a mixture of regret, and guilt, and an effort to harden his heart.

A. E. van Vogt

Afterwards, King Jim talked to him, and spoke of the uneasiness of everybody, and of the feeling that now the other linds would take revenge. 'But,' he said, 'I've pointed out how easily they were tricked once somebody like you set about doing it. How you pulled us up there, and hid us, before you confronted Vrain. And how it just took me and a few men up there. And how we merely waited until you and Vrain came aboard, and of how all six of us jumped him as he stepped out into the hall. And he couldn't use his weapons when you put that twenty-second delay on him.

'Like you said,' the older man finished, 'that one wire lifted six of us aboard the lind at one time, and that's all we needed. A tough army of six determined grounders.' His brown gaze sought Price's steely grey. 'But how do we know we can trust you and Kosorov not to use the captured linds like the others – the lind masters – did, once they got control?'

Price smiled grimly. 'I think I've got something for you on that. I'm going to put the voice of one of my computers on this outside speaker.' He pointed at the little object dangling from his neck, like a small locket. He went on, 'Normally, these things are automatic on a strictly literal organ by organ, gland by gland, and so on reaction. But we can ask for a general response. Listen.'

He pressed a button on the side of the 'locket'.

The voice that came out of it said, 'Essentially, Olin Price, your intentions are to rectify the wrongs of our devastated planet, and to rebuild on the basis of everyone sharing equally.'

The pressing fingers pushed the button again, and there was no more voice until his own spoke out upon the wilderness: 'When I originally conspired with Kosorov, I made him do that for me. At that time he gave the same reply.'

He stood there, and he looked into the relaxing faces around him; and he thought: 'Two linds down, and 136 to go.'

He turned away. 'I'd better get back up there. My wife has no idea of any of this. And I have to make my peace with her before I tell her.'

'Maybe,' he was thinking as he walked to the wire, 'I won't tell her at all'.

It was, he realized, not a good thought. But, being a human being and not a computer, it was the best he could do.

The Still Small Voice Inside

David Langford

... a small metal cube above his left ear.

Infield supposed it was a Cure, although he had never issued one like it. He didn't know if it would be good form to inquire what kind it was.

'It's a Cure for alcoholism,' Price told him. 'It runs a constant blood check to see that the alcohol level doesn't go over the sobriety limit.

'What happens if you take one too many?'

Price looked off as if at something not particularly interesting, but more interesting than what he was saying. 'It drives a needle into my temple and kills me.'

JOE HARMON, *Name Your Symptom.*
(Galaxy Publishing Corporation, 1956)

On the bright side:

Future Man is nothing special to look at. His clothes are a trifle oddly cut, perhaps, but his cranium does not balloon with the bulging lobes beloved of earlier S F artists. Ask him for the square root of some huge number, though, and he snaps out the answer. In his head is a calculator which cannot be dropped or stolen, which needs no free hand to operate. A version of telepathy is among the optional extras; advice on every subject is available at the drop of a thought; Future Man, though his privacy is always safe, need never be alone.

The other side:

Future Man 2 once stole. Very soon he was released and returned to his assembly-line work, which he now performs with vastly greater efficiency. In his head, an infallible watcher analyses his brain-rhythms, seeking always for the pattern of guilt, the knowledge of wrongdoing. Should Future Man 2 contemplate evil, he will be rewarded with blinding pain. It is some time since he last thought of anything but work, and food, and sleep. His dreams too have become pure . . . Before his sentence ends, the lesson will be irrevocably learnt; new thoughts will not be possible.

The gadget which makes either future possible is the bionic-implant computer terminal – biocomp for short, perhaps. Probably about the size of a postage stamp and a millimetre or two thick, the biocomp sits just beneath the skull. Fine wires lead from it to the appropriate parts of the brain, carrying the minute currents which dispense pleasure and information to the first Future Man, information and pain to the second. Body data can be gathered directly and simple decisions taken by internal programmes – 'Your body temperature is 102.2 degrees Fahrenheit, go to bed at once' – but the biocomp's own machine intelligence is limited by considerations of size and power. If one wishes to play a mental game of chess, or to be reminded of the titles of all A. E. van Vogt's stories since 1950, communication with a larger computer is needed; by means of a radio link with a time-sharing system, the effect of the little biocomp can be to bring the capabilities of this vastly more powerful machine into the owner's head.

At the present moment, this seems fairly unlikely. There are great difficulties regarding size, the power-source and the heat dissipation of the biocomp itself; even more formidable are the social and medical problems of mass brain surgery! (In Brian Aldiss's novel *The Primal Urge* it is relatively easy to swallow the notion of everyone in Britain wearing a little emotion-indicator light; the part that had to be glossed over rather rapidly was the drilling of a hole in every British skull . . .)

The three major mechanical problems – size, power, heat – are inevitably linked. Computers in general are much larger than they theoretically need be. A typical computer looks like a row of squat filing cabinets; within are endless wired connections between stacked circuit boards; on each board, integrated circuits balance on the spidery legs of eight to forty leads. And inside the epoxy case of each I C is the important part: a flat 'chip' of silicon up to an eighth of an inch square, carrying tens of thousands of transistors. The essence of a computer is an enormous number of such chips, arranged inches apart in a three-dimensional grid and separated by essentially irrelevant pieces of insulation or empty space.

This great mass of wiring is demanded by economics: the cost of designing and producing a silicon chip circuit is large, so general-purpose circuits are needed. A whole circuit board, or two, might be replaced by half a square inch of silicon (this is called L S I – large scale integration); but if that board is required in just one place in one computer, and there are many hundreds of similar but not identical boards to be boiled down to L S I chips, the price becomes prohibitive. On the other hand, if there is a huge demand for one L S I circuit, the price can fall rapidly: thus the electronic calculator. Thus too the biocomp, if the demand is ever great enough.

Like everything in the real world, L S I has its limits. Dropping the question of economics for the moment, imagine a medium-sized computer on a single silicon wafer. This is *really* large-scale; the wafer might be a foot across. (They can't be made so large at present, actually.) When the power is turned on, the wafer warms up ... in fact, it dissipates thousands of watts in its miles of internal connections, and destroys itself. Or if the power source is small and cannot provide this energy, the computer simply fails to work.

For a reasonably 'intelligent' biocomp, we need L S I circuitry operating at very low power. Naturally, owing to energy problems in general, there is continuous research into power consumption, and the requirements are gradually being reduced – nevertheless *some* power will always be needed. This could come, most simply, from batteries (slipped into a slot behind the ear? – just possibly) or a small radioisotope cell (lasts a lifetime, but you have to be tattooed with radiation warnings); some form of beamed-power pick-up might also be feasible.

A less obvious problem is that of chemical damage; the internal environment of the body is essentially salt water, a highly corrosive substance, at an elevated temperature which augments chemical reactions. The biocomp's input/output leads would be particularly endangered; carefully chosen, inert, expensive materials will be in demand–gold for example, with plastics like PTFE (polytetrafluoroethylene) when insulation is needed.

All these difficulties are simply that: difficulties. The mechanical problems of a biocomp *will* be solved, if only for medical reasons – without treating the device as an unnecessary luxury or a means of oppression, it could be a valuable aid in many of its simpler manifestations. The diabetic hears a warning buzz as his blood sugar reaches dangerous levels; the heart case, walking in the street, is advised to sit down for a few minutes; from the camera on the blind man's shoulder, signals are transmitted to provide a simulation of sight ...

An aid for the blind does exist, not unlike this last suggestion: here visual signals are converted into an electronic matrix which might be displayed as a pattern of dots (like a magnified newspaper photograph) – this pattern is passed to an array of small vibrators which form a 'touch-picture' on the blind man's back. Through long training he learns to interpret this and can, in a way, see.

This suggests how one might learn to use a biocomp, interpreting the messages it feeds into the brain. Since all nerves converge to the brain, the message could be anything: a twinge of one toe, a flash of red at the corner of the eye, the smell of peppermint or the sound of engines. The biocomp must likewise learn the language of its owner's brain. To oversimplify, there would perhaps be an initial session in which the owner is instructed to think in sequence, 'One ... Two ... Three ...' and so on through numbers and symbols, while the biocomp 'memorizes' the brain-pattern corresponding to each (the process called 'interfacing' in Michael Crichton's *The Terminal Man*). Then, on the simplest level, one would *think* a problem: 'One Two Three Times Four', for example, and straightaway the answer would come – *flash-of-red*/*beep*/*tickle-in-nostrils* – which the trained user would know at once was 'Four Nine Two' (492). A more advanced biocomp would be interfaced in both directions, so the machine

31

was trained to emit signals corresponding to one's own internal representation of symbols: one would *hear* the answer 'Four Nine Two'.

But, of course, the blind-aid mentioned above also suggests a simpler form of interfacing, one which does not require surgery on the brain. A biocomp just beneath the skin, under one ear, could perform many functions by picking up vibrations in the skull (the user's own voice: he can vocalize or subvocalize his problems) and relaying answers or information via a voice-synthesizer to the sensitive bone behind the ear. The effect would be of a voice in one's ear, as in van Vogt's story, a voice not audible to others.

Even simpler, a stage closer to the present day, the biocomp could be entirely detachable, built into – say – a pair of glasses. Many of the technical problems have been solved at this level in the course of improving hearing-aids and other miniature devices. This would not of course, be a 'bionic-implant-computer-terminal' but an advanced, talking electronic calculator.

The more sophisticated calculators of today can also transmit data to, and accept data from, larger computer systems: add a radio link, and one can talk to the big machine as easily as to the small. A little organization in the main computer, and the calculator becomes a means of instant communication with any other such calculator (and of course the other owners): electronic telepathy. Add library-data banks to the main computer, add public service programs, games-playing capabilities, an automated advice bureau, an electronic calendar and clock ... and the talking calculator in the frame of one's glasses becomes very attractive. Even if you don't wear glasses.

This is not far removed from the 'bright side of the future' described at the beginning of this piece. Escalation on such a scale has already been seen in the common, everyday calculator, which went in a few years from plain arithmetic to complex statistical functions, multiple memory stores and programming capability. And in every area – microelectronics, programming, communications – this super-calculator is a reasonable probability, within the grasp of present techniques. It may be inevitable. It is not science fiction!

The next jump is the greatest. The product so far of extrapolation is a biocomp in all respects but one: it is still on the wrong side of the skin. Medical monitoring is the most plausible route to the implanted version – for example, there's a traditional relationship between power and wealth (and the ability to pay for the first, expensive biocomps) and high blood pressure, heart trouble, etc. Continuous monitoring seems an excellent reason for the implant – 'Take it easy, your blood pressure has risen by thirteen per cent in the last ten minutes' – with the microprocessor (a mini-computer on a single silicon chip) inside the body, the extra computing facilities can be added by way of sugar coating. From there, the biocomp could slip into the logarithmic-spiral growth of the calculator: catching on as a status-symbol for anyone with, say, £5000; falling prices once a demand is established; a status-symbol for £1000; higher production and lower prices – and all the while, more frills appear. The still small voice in the ear informs that there are ninety-two milligrams of alcohol per millilitre of blood; that the toxins of fatigue are accumulating and sleep would be wise; that *bzzzzz!* the board meeting begins in ten minutes.

Now when a technique is esoteric and rare – the present state of brain surgery and of bionics – there is little chance of its being abused or perverted. Widespread acceptance of the biocomp would, however, render the techniques commonplace: the analogy becomes that of the back-street abortionist. The back-street biocomp surgeon might add an extra current-carrying lead into the rhinencephalon, the sensory nexus of the brain, and achieve the old S F cliché 'direct stimulation of the pleasure centres'. (In experiments where rats were permitted to give themselves such stimulation by pressing a lever, the creatures often enjoyed it so much that after pressing thousands of times an hour in preference to food or drink, they starved.) The 'wirehead' (Larry Niven's term) is likely to be less of a problem than the junky, though: even if the implantation were cheap, there is no way of leading up to it as there is with drugs. No samples – the potential wirehead must be convinced without demonstration that this wire will give him what he wants . . .

Thus the most likely form of private abuse. The irrevocable step, however, comes when a government decrees that in certain circumstances a biocomp is compulsory. There would be a long pause and much consultation before the step was taken; yet the old argument behind all repression, 'It's for your own good', is enduringly potent. It is certainly good that an inbuilt encephalographic monitor should warn the epileptic that *now* is the time to lie down and wedge a rubber pad between his teeth. It is probably good that the homicidal maniac could safely be allowed to roam, electronic tranquillization sending him into icy calm whenever the madness rises. It is questionably good – and yet how logical! – that the former thief should be *unable* to enter certain areas (as: strongrooms, empty shops, banks other than his own) thanks to the efficient biocomp, which hears the short-range radio signal NO ENTRY and issues a sharp, painful reminder should its owner attempt to trespass. (Meanwhile, of course, the back-street surgeon industriously removes these connections – at a price.) Electronic pleasure must have good uses, replacing anaesthetics in minor surgery and easing pain for the convalescent and the dying; a twist of programming, however, and the biocomp carefully generates a sensation of well-being as the owner's eyes fall on a particular politician or a particular breakfast cereal; subtly, the attitudes of the nation change. And every politician knows that *his* election is for the public good . . . If the lever exists, there is a constantly growing temptation to use it.

Fundamentally, no barrier exists between now and this dubious future. This is still an age of technological enthusiasm (despite the increasing energy problem) and it is probably fair to say of the biocomp and a number of other things, 'Since it can be done, it will be done' – though the device may be severely restricted by social forces, such as a fear of the escalation suggested above. Microelectronics has a record of pulling impossibilities from the hat – the cruise missile, for example, with the 'impossible' accuracy to strike within 40 feet of its target at 2000 miles, or the hand-held electronic chessplayer recently announced.

It is likely that by the end of the century, there will be people with that still small voice inside. That's the easy part of the prediction: the hard part is, what will it be saying?

Immune Dreams

Ian Watson

Adrian Rosen returned from Thibaud's sleep laboratory with a stronger presentiment than ever that he was about to develop cancer. He wasn't so much anxious about this, as simply convinced of it as a truth – and certain, too, that in some as yet ill-defined way he was partly in control of these events about to take place inside his body . . .

'It's obsessional,' Mary Strope grieved. 'You're receding – from me – from reality. I wish you'd give up this line of research. This constant brooding is vile. It's ruining you.'

'Maybe this recession into myself is one of the onset symptoms,' Rosen meditated. 'A psychological swabbing-down and anaesthetizing before the experience?' He lit another of the duty-free Gitanes he'd brought back from France and considered the burning tip. The smoke had no time to form shapes, today. It was torn away too quickly by the breeze, which seemed to be smoking the cigarette on his behalf – as though weather, landscape, and his own actions concurred perfectly. The hood was down, the car open to the sky.

They sat in silence and watched the gliders being launched off the hilltop, this red-haired, angular woman (fiery hair sprouting upon a gawky frame, like a match flaring) and the short burly man with heavy black-framed sunglasses clamped protectively to his face as though he had become fragile suddenly.

The ground fell away sharply before them, to reappear as the field-checked vale far below. The winch planted a hundred yards to their right whined as it dragged a glider towards it and lofted it into the upcurrents, to join two other gliders soaring a mile away among the wool-pack clouds. As the club's Land-Rover drove out from the control caravan to retrieve the fallen cable, Rosen stared at the directional landing arrows cut in the thin turf, exposing the dirty white chalk – in which the ancient horse, a few miles away, was also inscribed. Beyond, a bright orange wind-sock fluttered. Pointers . . .

'You don't even inhale,' Mary snapped. 'You could give up overnight if you were really worried.'

'I know. But I won't. I'm seeing how near a certain precipice I can edge before . . . the lip gives way. It needn't be lung cancer, you know. It needn't have anything to do with cigarettes . . .'

How could he explain? His smoking was only metaphorical now. Cigarettes were a clock; a pacemaker of the impending catastrophe. In fact, he was fairly sure that it wouldn't be a smoker's cancer at all. But it sounded absurd whenever he tried to explain this.

Then, there were the dreams . . .

Rosen stood before the blackboard in the seminar room of the Viral Cancer Research Unit attached to St David's Hospital and sketched the shape of catastrophe upon it with a stick of squeaky chalk that reminded him irresistibly of school days and Algebra lessons . . . The difficulty he'd had at first in comprehending x and a and b! His childish belief that they must equal some real number – as though it was all a secret code, and he the cryptographer! But once presented as geometry, mathematics had become crystal clear. He'd been a visualizer all along . . .

On the blackboard was the cusp catastrophe of René Thom's theorem: a cliff edge folding over, then under itself, into an overhang impossible on any world with gravity, before unfolding and flattening out again on a lower level. The shape he'd graphed was stable in two phases: its upper state, and its lower state. But the sinusoidal involution of the cliff would never allow a smooth transition from the upper to the lower state; no smooth gradient of descent, in real terms. So there had to be discontinuity between the top and the bottom lines of the S he'd drawn – an abrupt flip from State A to State B; and that was, mathematically speaking, a 'catastrophe'.

(There is no gravity in dreams . . .).

He waved a cigarette at his colleagues: Mary Strope, looking bewildered but defiant; Oliver Hart wearing a supercilious expression; Senior Consultant Daniel Geraghty looking frankly outraged.

'Taking the problem in its simplest mathematical form, is this a fair representation of the onset of cancer?' Adrian demanded. 'This abrupt discontinuity, here? Where we fall off the cliff –'

Rapping the blackboard he tumbled Gitanes ash and chalk dust down the cliff. The obsession with this particular brand had taken hold of him even before his trip to France, and he'd borrowed so many packs from the smoking room downstairs (where a machine was busily puffing the fumes from a whole range of cigarettes into rats' lungs) that Dr Geraghty complained he was sabotaging the tests and Oliver Hart suggested flippantly that Adrian should be sent to France *tout de suite*, Thibaud-wards, if only to satisfy his new craving . . .

'I suggest that, instead of a progressive gradient of insult to our metabolism, we abruptly flip from one mode to the other: from normal to malignant. Which is perfectly explicable, and predictable, using catastrophe theory. Now, the immune system shares one major formal similarity with the nervous system. It too observes and memorizes events. So if we view the mind – the superior system – as a mathematical network, could it predict the onset of cancer mathematically, *before* we reach the stage of an actual cellular event, from this catastrophe curve? I believe so.'

He swivelled his fist abruptly so that the stick of chalk touched the blackboard, rather than the cigarette. Yet it still looked like same white tube. Then he brought the chalk tip screeching from the cliff edge down to the valley floor.

Their eyes saw the soft cigarette make that squeal – a scream of softness. Adrian smiled, as his audience winced in surprise.

'But how can the mind voice its suspicions? I suggest in dreams. What are dreams for, after all?'

'Data processing,' replied Oliver Hart impatiently. 'Sorting information from the day's events. Seeing if the basic programmes need modifying. That's generally agreed –'

'Ah, but Thibaud believes they are more.'

Oliver Hart was dressed in a brash green suit; to Adrian he appeared not verdant and healthy, but coated in pond slime.

'For example, to quote my own case, I am approaching a cancer –'

Deftly, with sleight of hand, Adrian slid the cigarette off the cliff edge this time, amused to see how his three listeners braced themselves for a repeat squeal, and shuddered when it didn't come.

'I shall have the posterior pons brain area removed in an operation. Then I can act out my dreams as the slope steepens towards catastrophe –'

Mary Strope caught her breath. Stared, horrified.

'Enough of this rubbish, man!' barked Geraghty. 'If this is the effect Thibaud's notions have on you, I can only say your visit there was a disaster for the Unit. Would you kindly explain what twisted logic leads you to want part of your brain cut out like one of his damn cats? If you can!'

'If I can ... No, I couldn't have it done in France itself,' reflected Adrian obliquely. 'Probably it'll have to be in Tangier. The laws are slacker there. Thibaud will see to the arrangements ...'

Mary half rose, as though to beat sense into Adrian; then sank back helplessly, began crying, as Geraghty bellowed:

'This is a disgrace! Don't you understand what you're talking about any more, man? With that part of the brain destroyed there'd be no cut-off in signals to the muscles during your dreams. You'd be the zombi of them! Sleepwalking may be some temporary malfunction of the pons – well, sleepwalking would be nothing to the aftermath of such an operation! Frankly, I don't for one instant believe Thibaud would dare carry it out on a human being. That you even imagine he would is a sorry reflection on your state of mind! Stop snivelling, Mary!'

'Adrian's been overworking,' whimpered Mary apologetically, as though she was to blame for his breakdown, whereas she had only been offering love, sympathy, comradeship.

'Then he shall be suspended, *pro tem*. D'you hear that, Rosen? No more waltzing off to France, making fools of us.'

'But I shan't be living long,' Adrian said simply. 'You forget the cancer –'

'So there, we have located it,' Jean-Luc Thibaud had declared proudly, 'the mechanism that stops nerve signals from the dream state being passed on as commands to the body. Essentially the pons is a binary switching device. The anterior part signals that dreams may now take place, while the posterior part blocks off dream signals to the muscles . . .'

Thibaud seemed a merry, pleasant enough fellow, with a twinkle in his eye and the habit of raising his index finger to rub the side of his nose, as though bidding for cattle at some country auction. His father was a farmer, Adrian remembered him saying. And now his son farmed cats, not cattle.

'Thus we can remain relatively limp during our nightly dance with the instinctual genotype which psychologists so maladeptly label the unconscious mind . . .'

A hall of cats.

Each cat was confined in its own spacious pen, the floor marked off by a bold grid of black lines like graph paper. Lenses peered down, recording every movement the animals made on video tape.

Most cats were asleep, their eyes closed.

Most cats were also on the move. Scratching. Spitting. Arching their backs. Lapping the floor. Fleeing. Acting out their dreams in blind mute ritual dances of flight, rage, hunger, sexuality . . .

And a few, a very few, were only dozing, not dreaming. These didn't move. They hadn't drifted far enough down the sleep gradient yet. Soon they too would rise, and pace, and fight. Soon they too would lap the floor and flee. Till they dreamed themselves to death, from sheer exhaustion. It was tiring work, dreaming, down on Thibaud's cat farm.

From each cat's shaven skull a sheaf of wires extended to a hypermobile arm, lightly balanced as any stereo pick-up, relaying the electrical rhythms of the brain to be matched against this dream ballet taped by the video machines.

'And still I am dissatisfied, M'sieur Rosen! Still, we see only the genetic messages for the most basic activities being reinforced. That's what this is, you realize? A genetic reinforcement. Errors creep in from one cell generation to the next. Too many errors, and – pouf! An error catastrophe. Death. So dreams strive to reinforce the purity of the genotype – like the athlete trying to keep himself fit by exercises. Dreams are error correction tapes manufactured out of each day's new experiences. But gradually we begin to dream of the past, as the years go by. Increasingly we scavenge yesteryear. Soon, we are scavenging yesteryear's dreams themselves – using bygone, frayed correction tapes. We lose the capacity to make new ones. We dream vividly of childhood and it seems we are re-entering paradise as we sleep. Alas, that's all too true. We're about to leave the world, literally – for the cold clay of the cemetery.'

'Yet I wonder, Dr Thibaud, what if error is an essential part of our life process? What if, in order to be able to grow, we must also be able to die?'

'Yes indeed – the cruel dialectic of Nature!'

'Well then, what part has the cancer cell to play? It's the only truly immortal cell. It alone copies itself perfectly, without any error. And it kills us by doing so.'

'The difference between cell replication and cell differentiation is a knife edge we must all balance on, M'sieur Rosen.'

'Yet we all have cancer, potentially. Viral cancer lurks in everyone's cells in a latent form, did you know? I want to know, why? Doctors perpetually set themselves up to *cure* cancer – to *cure* polio, to cure everything else they label as disease. And that's supposed to be the whole work of medicine. But how many doctors ever trouble to glance at the whole system of life and evolution that a "disease" functions in? None whatever!'

A cat – a mangy, skinny alley-tabby – pounced on the invisible prey that it had been wriggling its way towards all the time they talked. But almost at once it leapt away again. Its fur stood on end, its tail bushed out, as it backed cowering into the corner of its pen.

'Did you see that, M'sieur Rosen? You could call it a catastrophe, in your terms – that sudden switch from fight to flight. The mouse becoming a monster in its mind: Yet how much do we really see? It's as you say about medicine – scratching the surface. Examining the arc of the circle and thinking that's all there is to the figure! But the inner landscape of the dream must be just as important as the actions. If not more so! In fact, I'm inclined to think the full subtleties of the genotype can only be coded into the dream as environment. Yet how to show that? Still, we're only starting on our journey inwards. Come, see the darkroom. We raise some other cats in black light and isolation from birth, so that they display the perfect archetype of a dream . . .'

The alley-tabby awoke, as they retraced their steps, and whined from the fretful exhaustion of having slept.

'Presumably, in an archetypal setting . . .'

Their glider bounded over the turf as the winch driver heeded the blinking of the aldis lamp from the control caravan, then slid smoothly into the air, climbing gently towards and upward of the winchgear. Mary pulled back softly on the stick, increasing the angle of climb to balance the downpull of the cable, till at eighty degrees to the winch and an altitude of a thousand feet she dipped the nose briefly, pushed the cable release knob, then climbed away.

'What if it doesn't let go?'

'It disconnects automatically, if you're at a right angle to the winch – which you shouldn't let happen.'

'It could jam.'

'There's a weak link in the chain, Adrian. By design. It's fail-safe.' But she sounded exasperated.

The hill upcurrent sent the glider climbing towards scattered woolly cumulus in a sky which was the blue of a pack of French cigarettes, as Mary manipulated the controls efficiently, banking, centralizing and taking off rudder, then repeating the same turning manoeuvre with a minimum of slip and skid. And so they spiralled aloft.

Her hair blazed back in the wind when the glider did slip to the right briefly on one turn, uncovering the firm rhombus of her cheek-bones, and a number of small brown moles just in front of the hair line. For a redhead her skin was only lightly freckled. It resembled the grain of an old photograph more than distinct freckles. Adrian loved touching and stroking those few hidden blemishes when they were in bed together, but it generally took a strong wind to whip the bonfire of hair back from them.

'So you're set on going to France?' she asked at last. 'I think Geraghty would rather Oliver went.'

'Oliver doesn't have my special interest.'

'What interest? It's nonsense!'

'You know very well.'

'I know nothing of the sort! You're perfectly healthy. Why else do you refuse to take a medical? It would show how wrong you are.'

'I can ... examine myself. The dreams, you see. It would spoil everything to have some silly check-up. Ruin the experience. I must keep perfectly clear and neutral.'

The glider skidded badly then, as Mary angrily used a bootful of rudder, and the nose began hunting, pitching to and fro.

'You realize you're wrecking our relationship? Your scientific credibility too! If that matters to you!'

'My dreams have a shape to them. I have to ... live them out.'

Correcting the trim of the machine, Mary spiralled the glider through the wool-pack, avoiding entering cloud. They soared above the snow cocoons into open sky; the clouds swept by below them now like detergent froth on rivers of the air – the vale and Downs being the soft clefted base of this surge of translucent streams. They continued a stable upward helix for another few hundred feet till uplift weakened and Mary swung the machine away towards a thermal bubble on which another pilot was rising a mile away, in company with dark specks of swifts and swallows catching the insects borne up along with the air.

But if they'd entered cloud, reflected Adrian, and if another pilot had also done so, and the curves of the two gliders intersected in the woolly fog, then there'd have been ... discontinuity: a catastrophe curve.

Marguerite Ponty accepted the infra-red goggles back from Thibaud and Rosen to hang on the hook outside the second of two doors boldly labelled DÉFENSE D'ÉCLAIRAGE!

The slim woman's dark glossy eyes were heavily accented by violet eye shadow which made huge pools of them; as though having spent too many hours in null-light conditions tending to the darkroom cats, her senses were starting to adapt.

Her hair was short and spikey, gamine-style. She wore dirty plimsolls, blue jeans and a raggy sweater under her white labcoat, the loops of the knitting pulled and unravelled by cats' claws. From her ears hung magnificent golden Aztec pyramids of ear-rings. Her scent was a strange mix of patchouli and cat urine: clotted sweetness and gruelly tartness grating piquantly together.

'The pons area is lesioned at one year old,' Thibaud commented. 'They've never seen anything. Never met any other cat but their mother. Yet in their dreams they prowl the same basic genetic landscape. The computer tells us how they show the same choreography – only purified, abstracted. What is it, I wonder? A Paul Klee universe? A Kandinsky cosmos? Has anyone unwittingly painted the genetic ikons?'

'Let's hope not Mondrian,' laughed Marguerite. 'What a bore!'

'Blind people dream,' Rosen reminded him. 'Surely they don't visualize. They smell, they hear, they touch.'

'And out of this construct their landscape, yes. Same thing. It's the putting together that matters. The shaping.'

'Topology.'

'Exactly. I was only using a metaphor. Let me use another: our blacklight cats are dancing to the same tune as our sighted tribe. Yet they experience next to nothing in their lives.'

Rosen couldn't help glancing pointedly at Marguerite Ponty's looped and raggled sweater. They experienced her.

'Which proves that dreams are control tapes for the genes, not ways of processing our daily lives. But come. Time to show you our cancer ward. We use nitrosoethylurea to induce tumours of the nervous system – thus the immune battle is fought out within the memory network itself! The basic instinctive drives yield right of way to a more urgent metabolic problem. You'll see the shape of catastrophe danced. That's what you came for.'

Rosen grinned.

'Immune dreams, yes. But what landscape do they dance them in?'

'Ah, there you ask the vital question.'

Another day. Another flight. Another landing. And Rosen had been to France, by now.

Mary pointed the glider down steeply towards the two giant chalk arrows cut in the field.

It struck him that she was diving too steeply; but not so, apparently, for she raised the nose smartly to bring them out of the dive flying level a few feet above the ground, the first arrow passing underneath them, then the second. They slowed as she closed the airbrakes, pulling the stick right back to keep the nose level, till they practically hovered to a touchdown so perfect that there was no perceptible transition between sky and ground. She threw the airbrakes fully open, and they were simply stationary.

Cursorily she rearranged her hair.

'Nature's so bloody conservative,' Adrian persisted. 'It has to be, damn it, or there wouldn't be any Nature! You can't have constant random mutations of the genotype. Or you'd always be losing on the swings what you won on the round-abouts. So once a particular coding gets fixed, it's locked rigidly in place. All the code shifts that have led from the first cells through to cabbages and kings, have operated upon redundant DNA, not the main genome. Look around, Mary. How diverse it all seems! Sheep. Grass. Birds, insects, ourselves. So much variety. Yet genetically speaking it's almost an illusion. Quality control is too strict for it to be any other way. Just think of the Histone IV gene for DNA protein-binding. That's undergone hardly any change since people and vegetables had a common ancestor a billion and a half years ago. Biological conservatism, that's the trick! But what's the most conservative cell we know?'

'Cancer, I suppose,' admitted Mary. 'What are you driving at now?'

'Quality-control to the nth degree!' he rhapsodized. 'That's cancer. And now we know there's viral cancer lying latent in everyone's cells. It's part of our genetic inheritance. Why, I ask you?'

'To warn the immune system,' Mary replied brightly. 'When a cell goes cancerous, the virus has a chance to show its true colours as an alien. Our immune system couldn't possibly recognize cancer as hostile tissue otherwise.'

'Very plausible! Then why's the system so damned inefficient, if we've got these built-in alarms? Why do so many people still die of cancer? Have medical researchers ever asked that, eh? Of course not! They never think about the whole system of life, only about correcting its supposed flaws.'

'Maybe more cancers get stopped early on than we realize?'

Adrian laughed.

'So you think we may be having low-level cancer attacks all the time – as often as we catch a cold? There's an idea! But I fancy that viral cancer's not locked up in our cells to warn the immune system at all. The reason's quite different. And it's so obvious I'm surprised no one's thought of it. Cancer's there to control the quality of replication of the genotype – because cancer's the perfect replicator.'

'That's preposterous!'

'Cancer isn't the alien enemy we think. It's an old, old friend. Part of the Grand Conservative Administration presiding over our whole genetic inheritance, keeping it intact! It's a bloody-minded administration, I'll grant you that. Has to be, to keep in power for a billion years and more. Thibaud was fascinated when I outlined my theory. It casts a whole new light on his genetic dream idea – particularly on the class we're calling "immune dreams". Cancer's a catastrophe for the individual, right enough. But for the species it's the staff of life.'

'Your health,' Thibaud grinned broadly: a farmer clinching a cattle deal. Marguerite Ponty smiled more dryly as she raised her glass, clicking her fingernails against it in lieu of touching glasses. Her earpieces shone in the neon light, priestess-like. Were they genuine gold? Probably. Her joke about Mondrian referred to her father's private collection, it transpired. Rich bourgeois gamine that she was, she'd chosen the role of a latterday Madame Curie of the dream lab – as someone else might have become a Party member, rather than a party-goer. There was something cruelly self-centred in the way she regarded Rosen now. Of the two, Thibaud was much more vulgarly persuasive . . .

Thibaud also looked genuinely embarrassed about the wording of his toast when the words caught up with him.

'A figure of speech,' he mumbled. 'Sorry.'

'It doesn't matter,' said Rosen. 'It's the logic of life – the cruel dialectic, as you say. Thesis: gene fixation. Antithesis: gene diversification. Synthesis: *ma santé* – the sanity of my body, my cancer.'

'Yours is such a remarkable offer,' Thibaud blustered, beaming absurd, anxious goodwill. 'You say an English specialist has already confirmed your condition?'

'Of course.' Rosen produced the case notes and passed them over. He'd experienced no difficulty forging them. It was his field after all. And if Thibaud suspects anything odd, thought Adrian, odds are he's only too willing to be fooled . . .

Still, Thibaud spent an unconscionably long time studying

the file; till Marguerite Ponty began flicking her gold earpieces impatiently, and tapping her foot. Then Rosen understood who had paid for much of Thibaud's video tape equipment and computer time. He and the woman regarded one another briefly, eye to eye, knowingly and ruthlessly. Finally, hesitantly, Thibaud raised the subject of the clinic in Morocco.

'It will take a little time to arrange. Are you sure you have time – to revisit England before you come back here?'

'Certainly,' nodded Rosen. 'I need to explain some more details of the theory to my colleagues. The cancer isn't terminal yet. I have at least two months . . .'

They sat in Mary's convertible, watching other gliders being winched into the air: close enough to receive a friendly wave from one of the pilots, whom Mary had been out to dinner with lately. A surveyor or estate agent or some such. Adrian hadn't paid much attention when she told him.

Or was he a chartered accountant?

The winch hummed like a swarm of bees, tugging the man up and launching him over the vale. Geologically speaking you'd classify it as a 'mature' valley. In a few more tens of thousands of years, weather action would have mellowed it beyond the point where gliders could usefully take advantage of its contours. But at this point in time there was still a well-defined edge: enough to cut the vale off from the hill, discontinuing, then resuming as the landscape below.

Mary lounged in the passenger seat. She was letting Adrian drive the car today. It was the least she could do, to show some residual confidence – since Geraghty's suspension of him; though it was some while since they'd actually been up in a glider together.

Softly, without her noticing, he reached down and released the handbrake.

Once she realized the car was moving of its own volition towards the edge, he trapped her hands and held them.

'Look,' he whispered urgently, 'the genetic landscape.'

'Adrian! This isn't a dream, you fool! You aren't asleep!'

'That's what they always say in dreams, Mary.'

He pinned her back in her seat quite easily with dreamlike elastic strength while she cursed and fought him – plainly a dream creature.

Soon the ground leapt away from the car's tyres; and he could twist round to stare back at the face of the hill.

As he'd suspected, it betrayed the infolded overhang of catastrophe. The shape of a letter S. Naturally no one could freewheel down such a hill . . .

Later, he woke briefly in hospital, his head turbaned in bandages, as seemed only reasonable after an operation to excise the posterior pons area of the brain. He found himself hooked up to rather more equipment than he'd bargained for: catheters, intravenous tubing, wires and gauges proliferating wildly round him.

He stared at all this surgical paraphernalia, curiously paralysed. Funny that he couldn't seem to move any part of him.

The nurse sitting by his bedside had jet-black hair, brown skin, dark eyes. He couldn't see her nose and mouth properly – a yashmak-like mask hid the lower part of her face. She was obviously an Arab girl. What else?

He shut his eyes again, and found himself dreaming: of scrambling up a cliff-face only to slide down again from the overhang. Scrambling and sliding. A spider in a brandy glass.

Infectious Science

John Taylor

I can recognize four main scientific ingredients in Ian Watson's story 'Immune Dreams', these being respectively cancer, the nature of the relation between mind and body, dreams and their relevance to health, and the mathematical study of discontinuous motion technically called catastrophe theory. Each of these involves an important area of modern scientific research as well as a great deal of past (and present) folklore. Before I attempt to come to terms with the science-fiction aspect of Watson's story, and, in particular, the feasibility of the technical aspects of the story, let me very briefly survey these four areas.

Cancer is the second leading cause of death in the Western hemisphere, after heart disease, and is more likely to kill than cerebral haemorrhage, accidents or infectious diseases. Yet though each of us is twice as likely to die from a heart attack as from cancer, most people feel that such a mechanical flaw is something we can understand. A similar acceptance of the other causes of death is also common; cancer alone is singled out as something which is totally mysterious and inexplicable and even a phenomenon of evil.

There are arguments to be raised both for and against this attitude. The implacable nature of the disease means that a human being has been condemned to death when told he has it. Worse, as the cancer progresses, he has to continue living weeks, months or even years with the knowledge that his days are numbered. Each new eruption of the disease in another part of the body will show he is losing the battle. Man seems very frail against such a force.

Nor has scientific understanding and control of cancer advanced at the pace it had been hoped. Vast sums of money have been poured into cancer research over the last two decades; many hundreds of millions of dollars each year, for example, in the United States. Yet a leading British researcher wrote in *Nature* recently, 'Nevertheless cancer research has so far had little effect on the outlook for patients suffering from most of the common cancers.' He added, 'The vast accumulation of knowledge about cancer and cancer cells is matched only by our abysmal lack of understanding . . .'

Yet scientific advances have been made, both in the nature of cures and in basic understanding. Some special forms of the disease have proved curable if caught early – Burkitt's lymphoma, usually affecting children in Africa, and choriocarcinoma, developing after pregnancy. The separate or combined uses of surgery, radiation and chemical treatment have saved the lives of several million of cancer sufferers throughout the world. The cellular basis of the disease has also been investigated and there is a clear understanding of where the crucial problems lie, especially of what causes the cancerous cell to commence its runaway division which ultimately kills the organism to which it belongs.

The mind and its relation to the body has been studied over the millennia by philosophers and theologians and latterly by scientists. The problem of how there can be control of matter by an incorporate entity has mainly given way to an analysis of how the brain can produce the complexity of behaviour that we see in the living forms around us. This shelving of the ancient mind–body problem has been done deliberately in brain research so that progress can be made on the body side of the duo. Indeed the ultimate thesis of brain research is that all behaviour can be ultimately understood in terms of the material brain.

The idea that there is only one, material, reality has had its adherents over the ages. Only very recently has this idea been seen to be capable of ultimate test in terms of scientific method, although many would say it was hubris to suppose that all experience could be reduced to a description in terms of atomic or molecular motions and reactions. Even some of those engaged in brain research would not accept that such a reduction would be possible, in practice or in principle. Yet that is the path which brain research is slowly treading. Up until now no barrier has been reached, and understanding of the way the various portions of the brain work together has advanced to allow for clinical application and the alleviation of much suffering.

As with cancer, the level of understanding of the relation of brain and activity is still pitiful in comparison with what is still to be understood. There is the story of a woman who suffered from a neurosis which required her to wash the outside walls, gutters and roof of her home at least once a week. Psychiatry, chemical treatment and group therapy all proved of no avail, so brain surgery was applied. After the operation the woman continued washing down the outside of her home, but now she sang while she did so.

There has been much interest recently in phenomena which appear to contradict normal science and possibly indicate some direct mental control over matter. It has even been claimed that these paranormal phenomena can occur only if there is a mental world separate from that of the body. I have been very interested in these strange events because of the severe challenge they present to the traditional scientific picture of the world, and also because they could offer a new window to the brain and its action. However, I do not think that there yet exists any hard evidence of the direct influence of mind over matter; what has been observed under reasonably careful conditions could still be explained inside standard science.

In classical antiquity people were accustomed to treat what we now call the manifest content of dreams as valid perceptions, believing that the persons and things they saw in dreams were real. They thought, for example, that gods must exist because they appeared in dreams. It was necessary to expel dreams from scientific consideration to advance an objective analysis of the world. That having been done, dreams have more recently returned as a valid area of analysis both from a psychological and also from a physiological aspect. Thus the content of a dream gives some indication of subconscious motives and problems important to an individual, as Freud first discussed in 1900 in his book *The Interpretation of Dreams*. Indeed these subconscious impulses are very likely released in the dream in a situation which allows them to be controlled. One psychiatrist even maintains, 'The dream is the normal psychosis and dreaming permits each and every one of us to be quietly and safely insane every night of our lives.'

The physiological centres of dream activity have also been investigated over the last two decades, ever since two, associated, objective indicators of dreaming – rapid eye movements and low-voltage, high-frequency brain waves – were discovered. Much has come from studies of the effects on dream activity and general behaviour of cats caused by the removal of certain portions of the brain; some areas have been discovered which apparently control the activity of dreaming.

These various approaches to dreaming also mirror the variety of theories of why we dream. On the psychological side is the idea of a release valve, and also the possibility that the sequence of dreams that everyone experiences through the night are involved in upgrading the general and rapid response mechanisms to take account of what has happened during the previous day. Physical explanations of dreams involve the need to remove some toxic material that has been accumulating during waking life; this explains the irritability which can arise if selective suppression of dream sleep occurs.

The final topic used by Ian Watson in his story derives from the general ideas of catastrophe theory developed over the last few years by the French mathematician René Thom. This is a mathematical analysis of the various ways that sharp or discontinuous motions, such as a wave breaking, occur. The simplest possibility is to visualize a skier going over an overhang; if he is moving very slowly he will suddenly drop down from the edge of the overhang to the depths below. It is the sharp drop which is called a catastrophe (as it will be when the skier hits the ground). Thom's contribution was to work out the various possible types of catastrophe that can occur. These are strictly limited to one – the cusp catastrophe – in our ordinary world; it is the motion suffered by the skier I mentioned above. In spaces of higher dimension the number of different types of catastrophe motion increases but is still severely limited. Thus in four dimensions there are three possible catastrophes, called the swallow-tail, elliptic umbilic and hyperbolic umbilic.

Catastrophe theory has proved of great value in visualizing the way a discontinuous change is actually occurring, and reducing its complexity. An example given by another mathematician, Christopher Zeeman, who has also contributed to catastrophe theory, is enlightening. It concerns the reactions of a dog, of flight or attack, in terms of its rage or fear. When it is frightened the dog will clearly retreat and only when it is very angry will it attack. But in a situation where it is both angry and frightened it may suddenly change its behaviour, say from flight to attack or vice versa. Such a discontinuous change can be analysed in terms of catastrophe theory, and appears to correspond to a cusp catastrophe.

Let me now turn to Ian Watson's story 'Immune Dreams' and consider its relation to the various scientific strands that I have discussed so far. The hero, or more suitably the anti-hero, Adrian Rosen, believes that he is about to have cancer and that he cannot stop it; at least he does not seem to wish to try but accepts the inevitable fate in store for him. He wishes, moreover, to have a portion of his brain removed so that he can act out this apparent catastrophe in his dreams so as to make it more vivid.

It is claimed, first of all, that cancer is locked up in each and every one of our cells in viral form. And secondly the reason it is there is 'to control the quality of replication of the genotype – because cancer is the perfect replicator'. Thirdly it is claimed that even before the runaway cell division occurs (which is a cancer developing) that the body can detect this, and that such knowledge can accordingly enter into dreams.

There are various theories existing as to what causes cancer. It is known that in some animals it is possible to induce cancer by a virus; thus leukaemia can be induced in mice, in fowl, and possibly in other animals, such as cattle, guinea pigs, cats and rats, by viruses. Leukaemia induced in a monkey has yielded large quantities of a herpes-like virus particle, identical in size, shape and other characteristics to those found in tissue cultures of human leukaemia. However there is no support at all for the claim that we all of us possess viral cancer for ourselves. Indeed if this had been proved to be the case there would undoubtedly be a vast amount of support for a crash programme to prevent leukaemia by using a vaccine similar to that used to prevent, for example, human influenza, polio and measles. But that is certainly not the situation at present. Of course it may well be that all cancers are shown to have a viral origin. The present understanding is that cancers may be caused by various sorts of chemicals, by viruses, by ionizing radiation, such as X-rays and gamma rays, and possibly by other environmental influences. It is not at all clear at this stage that there is a single *modus operandi* of cancer and indeed there may be a number. How it is that chemical carcinogens can apparently change the genetic reproductive capabilities of a cell is not at all apparent. There may not even be a change in the genetic structure for cell division but only in some important environmental feature of the cell itself. In other words Adrian Rosen, or should I say Ian Watson, may well be right after all that all cancer is caused by a virus of one form or another.

The second thesis of Ian Watson, that cancer controls the quality of replication, also appears to be rather dubious. This is because cancerous cells which are dividing rapidly may well have far more chromosomes than is normal. Indeed some have been seen with upwards of a thousand in the cell nucleus. Clearly if that is so, then an enormous modification has occurred of the genetic apparatus in the cell nucleus. The cause of such an increase of chromosome number and its precise relevance to the cancerous cell are not yet known. But this feature is clearly of importance as a critical clue to unlocking the cancer story. I can only repeat that cancer cells certainly seem to be the poorest replicators of all, except for their powers of division. That itself is a great defect in a living system which has to balance division against stability in numbers. Division should occur in a cell only when more numbers of it are needed due to wear and tear in the organs. Clearly the signalling mechanism indicating such needs must have broken down in some way in the cancerous state.

Finally, the question as to whether or not cancer in its overall development is a catastrophe is clearly false. A single cancerous cell will start to divide rapidly and each of its descendants will also be cancerous and so be in division. Yet one can follow the rate of change of the number of cells that are cancerous in an organism. It may well be that in the long term the growth of the number of cells appears to be catastrophic. Yet a growth curve is one which is smooth, and while there may be a billion cells that are developed from a single cancerous cell in a period of a year or so, there is no catastrophe, in the technical sense of the word, about such an augmentation. Thus it would appear that catastrophe theory in its technical form is not appropriate to the discussion of cancer. It may well be that it is, in the sense that it may be necessary to use the classifications of the forms of catastrophe to best appreciate and describe the way in which a single cell may suddenly become cancerous. However, such discussion will initially only be at the descriptive level. When it is necessary to investigate more fully all the steps in the causal chain which turn the cell from a normal one to a cancerous one, then the standard approach of scientific method must be used. A detailed model has to be set up and the process of change described more fully. Even then a switch from one state to another may well occur which would thus be a catastrophe. Yet it would be necessary to see in detail if such a discontinuous transformation would occur. At this stage it is not known if such is the case in the development of cancer.

A little is known about the feature of dreams which indicates the health of the body, at least as far as case histories are concerned. There are people who have dreamed that they have had a certain type of illness or have had cut away a certain painful portion of their body. Some little time later it has turned out that they have had a disease in the particular portion of the body about which they dreamt, possibly a tumour or an ulcer. This feature of dreams, of presenting to the mind features that are possibly below the normal conscious level occurring in the environment, both internal and external, is one which could be well developed by many of us.

The nature of dream control assumed by Rosen certainly appears very feasible. That the pons may control dream activity and prevent the actual physical working out of the dream content is a conjecture that could have some truth in it. There are dream centres located in that region whose destruction, apparently, prevents certain features of dreaming. Dreams can give an indication of the health of the person as well as his psychological state. Certainly I would warmly support any move to use dreams more actively in life to determine the nature of our activities in our waking periods.

It is possible to conceive a definite programme to achieve this. In the same manner that clinics for various forms of disease, such as venereal disease, have been set up and even use posters to advertise their existence and range of help, so a network of dream centres should be formed throughout the country and so advertised. The main purpose of such centres would be for people who have dreamt that they are ill, and are worried about it, to go and describe their dreams. As well as psychologists trained in dream interpretation at these 'sick-dream' centres, it would be necessary to have qualified doctors and, if possible, X-ray and similar diagnostic equipment.

Before such an organization were to be constructed, with corresponding cost, it would be necessary to initiate a pilot study to investigate the numbers of people with such dreams and the problems to be encountered in the analysis of the 'sick-dream'. Far too little is known about the subject to be able to say how many lives would be saved by early discovery of sickness through dreams, but even if it were only a small number of lives it would still be of great value.

Let me now turn to the way the mind is involved in discerning cancer at least as far as Adrian Rosen is concerned. He likens the mind to a mathematical network which can predict 'the onset of cancer mathematically before we reach the stage of an actual cellular event, from this catastrophe theory'. The mind thus acts as some sort of super-computer which can extrapolate ahead and indicate that the activity, especially of division, of the cells in the body is about to suffer a catastrophe. This is a very interesting thesis, although the mind, as far as I understand it, is not a mathematical network of any sort. If we liken it to a super-computer, then it might be possible for this computer to extrapolate ahead as to the future state of development. I think personally that this is rather unreasonable, especially because the amount of information needed to make such predictions would be enormous. It is more likely that the warning that arises in dreams, and which has been used in the story, comes from quite clear physiological changes at a reasonably gross level. Thus it is most probable that the dream presaging the onset of cancer has started when the cancer has already progressed to the size of a small lump, but one which would be large enough to be recognized locally in the tissue surrounding that area though not yet possibly at a large enough level to cause serious trouble.

The idea of dreams associated with data processing, which I mentioned earlier, is certainly very attractive and has been put forward a number of times so far, though has not yet been proven. This idea fits in more generally with the properties of the mind as a set of comparisons between ongoing and past events. The computational features involved in setting up such comparisons may be quite remarkable. I would still come back to the point that I do not feel it reasonable to regard the mind as sufficiently powerful to compute the developmental state of each and every one of the cells throughout the body, but that surely would be necessary for the catastrophe of cancer to be predicted.

I don't see anything infallible in the cancer that Adrian Rosen is expecting. He could well modify his environment in such a way that he could avoid it. It might even be that he would give up smoking! This should change the data going into the mind computer and hence could well lessen the possibility of a catastrophe occurring. Indeed it would be very difficult for any single person to predict some way ahead of time what their future state might be since they do not know the activities of others around them and of the environment. All sorts of pollution might occur which would destroy them very rapidly yet they would not appreciate that beforehand. Only if there is precognition can one expect such an infallibility about one's mind computer.

The use of catastrophe gives a dramatic force to the story, although it must be realized that there are far more than the single cusp catastrophe that is being used by Rosen. Only if there are two variables under control will the catastrophe be of cusp form. It is not clear how many variables are involved in the development of cancer and until that is clear it would not be possible to categorize the forms of catastrophe that are relevant. But in any case I don't think that the catastrophe is appropriate, as I said earlier, to the development of cancer, except at the change-over stage from a single cell into a cancerous state. I certainly cannot see how the mind computer would have enough information coming to it to indicate this catastrophic change at the single cell level.

These criticisms are ones of technical form alone. It does not lessen the imaginative use of recent scientific ideas put into a fictional form and the presentation of problems raised by such developments. However, I cannot respond to the hero's fatalistic submission to the environment, so I find myself sympathizing more with his scientific colleagues. It is they who are trying to make sense of the world. In particular, it is they who do not accept Rosen's conjectures in the same wholehearted way as he does. Indeed I would agree with Rosen's colleagues that he has in some ways 'freaked out' because he does act out his conjectures in the extreme. It would surely have been more appropriate, at least for a reasonable scientist, to have shown the truth of his conjectures concerning the nature of catastrophic development in cancer cells. Since Rosen is an expert in this area, it could possibly have proved to be a very valuable research project ... I suppose I feel that presenting scientists in an unfavourable light, always does a disservice to science, and to the scientific community. The Frankenstein and Doomsday syndromes are already too strongly with us. I can only recommend that scientists be looked at with more appreciation, and request Ian Watson to write a sequel to Rosen's adventures when he finally comes round from his accident in hospital. I will look forward to reading it with eager anticipation, and I hope I enjoy it as much as I enjoyed 'Immune Dreams'.

The Time Travellers

Isaac Asimov is interviewed by Christopher Evans

EVANS: How did you first get interested in science fiction?

ASIMOV: Oh quite accidentally I'm afraid. My father had a candy store all through my youth and when I was nine years old I noticed science fiction magazines on the news-stand. My father didn't allow me to read magazines in general, because he thought they represented cheap literature and my mind must not be spoilt by such things. But I did persuade him to let me read science fiction magazines by stressing the word *science* in the title. He was an immigrant and couldn't speak English very well, but he knew what science was. Our family came from Petrovihi, USSR, which is about fifty miles south of Smolensk, or about 200 miles south west of Moscow. I was born in 1920 and my parents came here to the United States with me in February 1923. So I was just about three years old when I arrived. I was educated here – I know no Russian, have no memory of the Soviet Union and have been an American citizen since 1928.

Anyway, as I said, I read science fiction for years, loved it. And almost anybody who reads science fiction avidly from, say, twelve on or from before twelve on, invariably tries to write it eventually. Actually, young people who read science fiction are apt to become fanatic about it, and in a surprising number of cases it becomes the *only* thing they read for a period of years. They look avidly for other readers so they can discuss it, they form clubs and societies, they attend conventions. It is almost a small subculture of its own – as in the case of the *Startrek* fad. But when you're involved in such a thing you want to become even more involved and the way in which you can become most involved is to become a writer. Science fiction writers are heroes to the young fans – they represent to them what movie stars represent to a great many more people, and they want to be science fiction writers the way so many young girls, let us say, want to become movie stars.

But the thing about science fiction that really distinguishes it from other cults for young people is the fact that it alone represents a kind of aristocracy of the intellect. All the other subcults – the movies, the Western heroes, wanting to be a railroad engineer in the old days or an aeroplane pilot now – represent a kind of apotheosis of beauty, of action, of muscle. Only science fiction, as far as I know, represents an apotheosis of the brain. This means that it attracts the youngsters who are bright in the school, who are interested in science, who are not good at sports, who are perhaps rather lonely because they don't get along in the rough-and-tumble of the world. Unfortunately there's also a temptation to go off into the fringes of science and therefore they get interested in flying saucers, in Velikowski, in ESP and so on. But I think the key point, the thing that makes them different from all others, is the emphasis on intellect.

EVANS: Yes, presumably there's a kind of intelligent broad-mindedness too, which does lead one almost to the trap of the flying saucer–ESP game. But was the type of literature that you were fed on initially the pulp magazines?

ASIMOV: Yes, but once I had discovered science fiction by way of my father's news-stand I became aware that there were writers who had already written science fiction which had appeared in *books*, and I got books by Verne and Wells out of the library. I must say that, as a youngster, I never found them so fascinating as the pulp magazines, which supplied my needs in a way that no book could. They came out periodically, every month on a specific day so that there was the tension of waiting for them; and they had fascinating covers. The stories were far more poorly written than Verne and Wells, but by the same token they somehow stimulated me more. I wasn't looking for excellent literature, I was looking for ideas and a sense of wonder. And one other thing which to me was very important – there were letters in the back of these pulp magazines written by other people like myself, which made me aware of the fact that I wasn't 'the only one'. Reading them was almost the most fascinating part of the entire magazine. Eventually, by the time I was fifteen, I even worked up the courage to write a letter of my own to a magazine, and it was published – so that my very first appearance in a science fiction magazine was in a letter column, about four years before I appeared as a writer.

EVANS: What was the first story that you actually wrote?

ASIMOV: The first story I wrote, 'Cosmic Corkscrew,' was never published as a matter of fact. It was only submitted to *Astounding Science Fiction* and they rejected it, and I never submitted it again. I don't possess it any more, I don't even know what happened to it. The second story I wrote, which I called 'Stowaway' but which was later given the title of 'The Celestian Menace', was eventually sold after some time. The third story I wrote, 'Marooned on Vesta', was actually the first story I *sold*. It appeared in the March 1939 issue of *Amazing Stories* and represents the first item of writing that I was paid for. The second of my stories to be sold was 'The Weapon Too Dreadful to Use'. It appeared in print only about six weeks after it was sold because *Amazing Stories* had a hole they had to fill in the May 1939 number. Somehow I never count these two, because *Amazing* was not the magazine I wanted to get into. I wanted to get into *Astounding Science Fiction* and I sold them my first story in December 1938. It appeared in the July 1939 *Astounding Science Fiction*, and its name was 'Trance'.

EVANS: It seems that already there was a separation out in the quality of the literature. Evidently for some reason you were really intrigued at the notion of getting into *Astounding Science Fiction* and considered *Amazing* to be almost a slightly different stream of science fiction. Is that correct?

ASIMOV: Oh yes indeed. Originally *Amazing* had been *the* aristocrat of science fiction, and it had called itself that.

Until about 1934 it was the best of the science fiction magazines, but then *Astounding* was taken over by Street and Smith and in about 1934 they began publishing the best science fiction in the world. This was increased to a new and even higher level when John W. Campbell became editor in 1938. Meanwhile *Amazing*, which had been going downhill for a number of years, was sold to Ziff-Davis which then put it out as a distinctly pulpish magazine. I don't mean pulpish in the sense that it was on pulp paper – they all were – but they deliberately geared the writing to a lower level of intellect. There was a third magazine called *Thrilling Wonder Stories* which stressed action rather than ideas, but *Astounding* was in a class by itself. Campbell insisted on good writing, on real characters, on scientists who thought, acted and talked like scientists. No doubt the real literary critics would have scorned what appeared in *Astounding*, but to us fans it was just the best – either before or since for that matter. Well, that was what I was aiming at, and that was what I finally made with my third published story.

As a matter of fact I was very fortunate because I lived at that time in Brooklyn, only a half-hour subway ride from John Campbell. I went there literally carrying my first story, not because I intended to see him but because I didn't know how submitting stories worked, and the only thing I could think of was to go there and hand it in to the editor in person. Heaven knows what I would have done if I had lived in Oshkosh or Butte, Montana or something! But when I got there he recognized the name because he had been publishing letters by me, and he asked me to come in to see him. I did, in a state of complete confusion. I had to go down a flight of stairs and then through a large warehouse-like building, between bales of papers and piles of magazines. I found him and then we sat and talked for two hours. Now, that was John Campbell for you. I discovered later that there was nothing he liked better than to talk. He would talk to anybody for any length of time. After that every time I had a new story I went in to see him. What it amounted to was that I got a kind of informal course in how to write science fiction from him.

I would like to think that without him I would still have learnt how to write but it would have taken much longer and would not have been as thrilling or as much fun.

EVANS: He really was one of the most significant figures in modern science fiction, wasn't he? What was there about him which made him so good and which made *Astounding Science Fiction* so successful as a magazine?

ASIMOV: John Campbell had a desire to dominate. He was a large man, but he seemed larger than he was – he was about six feet tall, but always seemed eight feet tall; he was a large man across too – he seemed to fill a room. He wanted science fiction to become something that *he* wanted. When talking to anybody, he always tried to force his ideas, his personality on them, and this wasn't difficult because he was overflowing with charisma. Even in his last years, when he was no longer dominating the field and when he had somehow lost touch a little with the currents in science fiction, you could still feel this power when you met him. He was never lost for words; he could take any idea, however ridiculous, and in some way defend it so that you couldn't knock it down even though it seemed so rickety. Although his social views, as a friend of mine sometimes said, were a little bit to the right of Attila the Hun, he was himself personally the kindest possible man. Well let's put it this way, I always view him as a kind of racist, and yet *never* in personal contact with him did he seem personally like a racist. In the same way I could never read his editorials. They were, it seems to me, invariably wrong-headed, and yet on the other hand there was no question that people loved them and that to refute those editorials was extremely difficult.

EVANS: They were almost the point at which science fiction had its foot in academic life weren't they? He used them to raise philosophic issues and to introduce the notion of logical argument to his readers.

ASIMOV: Well John himself always said that the importance of his editorials was that they made people think. Of course he was *persona grata* at M.I.T., where he was constantly visiting and lecturing, and in many other academic places too. In a very real sense he made science fiction *respectable*. Before John it had been sneered at by most people; even people who were willing to admit that there was something to Verne and Wells but thought that magazine science fiction was a kind of childish perversion of the *real* science fiction. When John Campbell came in he produced a kind of SF that adults and scientists could read without embarrassment. Until then the covers had been garish in order to catch the young eye (as they had caught mine). But he quickly decided that there were now enough mature readers around and produced covers that were subdued, respectable, sometimes beautiful. None of this business of having to tear the cover off so that you wouldn't get into trouble when you brought it home.

EVANS: He would take any idea of course, wouldn't he, and have a good look at it? This really led him, through being open-minded, down some strange pathways – I am thinking of the Hieronymous machine and in particular, of course, his flirtation with Dianetics and Scientology.

ASIMOV: Well I think the great tragedy of John's life was the fact that in the early 1940s he predicted that the most significant outcome of World War Two would not be which of the two sides won, but that atomic power would be developed. He was perfectly right. In a way this was unfortunate because it gave him the idea that he could see rather more clearly than he really could. After the war he realized that notions like interplanetary flight and nuclear power had really been used up in science fiction. He looked for something else, some new world to conquer, and he found it on the fringes of science. He found it first in Dianetics because this purported to be a new science of the mind, a kind of approach which he believed was as far beyond ordinary psychiatry as nuclear power was beyond fossil fuel power. John climbed on the fringe science bandwagon and somehow never got off. By the way, I think one mustn't underestimate the fact that he left M.I.T. not because of any failing in science, but because he had trouble passing the German requirement, the language requirement. He then went to Duke and it was in Duke that he got his degree, and it was in Duke, coincidentally, that Professor Rhine did his ESP work. Now, though I am not a psychologist, it seems likely to me that because John had been, so to speak, rejected by M.I.T. and accepted by Duke, he rejected that which M.I.T. symbolized – the physical sciences, engineering – and he accepted that which Duke symbolized – ESP, work on the fringes – and they finally won out.

EVANS: Yes. Just let's go back to Dianetics though – it was really through publishing Hubbard's original article in *Astounding Science Fiction* and through being so open-minded and tolerant that he actually launched Dianetics and Scientology on the world – it is particularly interesting isn't it, because Scientology is now clearly a religion and what's more, it's a religion based on the concepts of SF. Do you think that the cultish nature of SF inevitably led to a religion growing out of it? Are you surprised, in other words, to find Scientology what it is today?

ASIMOV: Well I'm always surprised to find irrationality doing as well as it does, but I think I'm slowly becoming accustomed to the thought that the rational mind is in such a small minority that you can't *ever* possibly expect it to win out. Obviously, science fiction can give rise to religious movements – not just Scientology. Von Daniken, for instance, has himself inspired a kind of religious cultishness – the worship of the ancient astronauts; the Velikowskian view has also become religiously tinted. All these things obtain such a hold over those who believe in them that they become not only religiously minded but strongly proselytizing, very intolerant of opposition, and very prone to seek religious martyrdom. But interestingly enough, the strongest opposition to these cults comes from science fiction people who resent having science fiction perverted in this way. Just as, for instance, when Christianity began as a kind of Jewish sect it was many of the Jews themselves who resisted most strongly – and do so to this day. In this way I suspect that when the science fiction religions finally become powerful there will be a group of secular science fictionists, the Jews of the science fiction world, who will resist and remain resistant. I feel that I would be one of them, if I lived long enough.

EVANS: The 1940s and the 50s most people see as having been the seminal years of science fiction. Do you agree with that? And if you do agree, would you say that there was a feeling of excitement amongst fellow science fiction writers, a realization that they were opening up people's minds to new ideas and pushing forward a whole new philosophy?

ASIMOV: Well the 40s and 50s do represent the golden age of science fiction. It was the last period, perhaps the last period *ever*, in which one could be optimistic about science. It was a time when you could see clearly that nuclear power was coming and then there it was; that we could reach the moon and we did; that there were computers which would become more and more powerful, and there they were. All the old plots of science fiction, the basic ones, seemed to be coming true. We, the writers, were in the forefront and it was a very exciting thing to be riding the wave.

EVANS: What I am trying to get at is were you aware of the fact that you were riding this wave, and were the other writers aware of this as well?

ASIMOV: John Campbell was aware, and he made *me* aware and I suspect he made the others aware too. I knew that people were investigating uranium fission with respect to atomic power, and had known it from 1941 – but only because John Campbell told me. I don't know how he knew, but that's how *I* knew. He told all his writers – and he got lots of nuclear power stories as a result. Willie Ley, who was a close friend of John Campbell and of science fiction writers, was quite aware of how close we were to achieving practical rocketry, and he made the rest of us aware. Yes, on the whole I think that we were aware of riding the wave, and as I've said, it was a great feeling.

Now since the 1950s a mood of pessimism has spread over science fiction. People don't want to write so much about the physical sciences, because it seems *passé*. It seems that science will catch up too quickly, that we are not really involving ourselves with something sufficiently new. This has led to a tendency to shift to all sorts of facets of possible or fringe science where we feel that real science won't catch up. So you did start getting an awful lot of stories based on ESP and an awful lot of social science fiction with very little real science in it. Then too, other factors intervened. Ordinary fiction began to die, the non-SF pulp magazines began to die in the 1940s, and the slick magazines in the 50s and 60s. The result is that there are very few places where you can get short stories published these days. Nowadays it's the paperback and the novel that's the big thing, and it's hard for young people to break in. When I was a kid the pulp magazines published hundreds of rotten stories every month, and that's the kind of stories that young kids can write – rotten stories. By writing the rotten stories, and having them published, they're encouraged to continue writing until they can write good ones. If you don't publish the rotten stories then they are not encouraged to write and they never learn how to write good ones. Well right now, the only outlet for short stories are science fiction magazines, so that a great many youngsters who are writing science fiction would not write science fiction at all had they a broader field of opportunity – they're not really interested in SF, but that's the only thing they can possibly sell. Of course the kind of science fiction they turn out is non-science, anti-science even. They specialize in stylistic experimentation, they're much more literary than they are science fictionish and they make up a whole new group that they call 'new wave', which is foreign to me.

EVANS: At what stage did you suddenly realize that you could really do something with science fiction and might even make a career out of it?

ASIMOV: Oh that really came very late in life. I didn't really think I could make a *career* of writing until after I had begun

69

to make a career as a professor of biochemistry. But I realized that I was going to be a good science fiction writer, whether I made a career of it or not, with the publication of 'Nightfall' in the September 1941 issue of *Astounding Science Fiction*. That was a kind of turning point. I had been a writer for three years at that time and had turned out a series of stories which weren't very bad, but which weren't very good either. They were good third-rate science fiction. Then came 'Nightfall'.

The reason I wrote it was because I had visited John Campbell with some completely different idea and he produced a quotation from Emerson concerning the possibility that if human beings could see the stars only once in a thousand years they would apparently fall down in awe and wonder and preserve for many generations the remembrance of the city of God. John, who specialized in turning things on their heads, said that, on the contrary, if people could see stars only once in a thousand years they'd go insane at this unlooked-for sight, and he suggested that I write a story about it. I went home and wrote 'Nightfall', which was a very unusual story in the sense that it sort of killed that particular plot for ever. Nobody had ever written a story like that before and nobody could ever write a story like that again. I was very fortunate to be able to have the chance to write it and it turned out to be surprisingly popular and has remained popular ever since. A few years ago the Science Fiction Writers of America voted on the best science fiction short stories of all time, and 'Nightfall' finished first by a wide margin.

It was a very simple plot really. It dealt with a world which had six suns so arranged that once every two thousand and something years the situation arose that there was only a single sun on one side of the planet – the remaining five being on the other – and it was at that time that there was an unexpected eclipse of that sun by an unknown satellite. The eclipse had the effect of plunging the entire planet into darkness for a period of one day so that *everyone* on the planet experienced darkness for the first time – and they all went mad. Therefore civilization proceeded in cycles. Every two thousand years or so there was a downfall and a rebirth. In this particular cycle somehow, by chance or by good luck, they had worked out the laws of gravity and determined the existence of the troublesome satellite, and thus could predict the eclipse. Therefore they started preparing a place of refuge equipped with artificial light, so that a limited number of people could sit through the period of eclipse without going mad. In this way they hoped they could then start a new cycle, while retaining the knowledge of the old cycle. The next cycle everyone would be prepared for, and there would be no further downfalls.

The story is just about the last four hours before the eclipse in which everybody says there's going to be an eclipse and everyone's going to go mad. The eclipse finally comes – and everyone goes mad. There's no suspense, no nothing. I once re-read the story to try to find out why on earth people should think it was so good, when frankly it was amateurishly written and, as I say, the plot was very simple. I think it was the sheer accident of the fact that I never actually ended a scene; in other words every scene was interrupted by the beginning of the next scene, which was then interrupted by the beginning of the next scene, so that through the entire story the reader never once had a chance to catch his breath – the effect was that of a toboggan ride downhill, faster and faster and faster to the catastrophe with no last minute rescues. I think maybe that's it. But in any case it was a turning point, and after that I knew I was a first-class science fiction writer.

EVANS: I must say (it doesn't diminish the brilliance of the story, which is also one of my favourites) I'm surprised to learn that the idea actually came from Campbell. Is there a good deal of exchanging of ideas, consciously and unconsciously, amongst science fiction writers, would you say, with the prize going to the person who makes the best thing out of either his own or someone else's idea?

ASIMOV: Well it's my experience that science fiction writers are very quiet about what they're writing. Partly it is because there is suspicion amongst writers (a good suspicion) that if you talk too much about what you're writing you're not going to write it, you blow off the steam. Furthermore, every writer knows that any other writer, with the best will in the world, will rarely be able to prevent himself from using the idea; he will talk himself into thinking that he's thought it up himself. So we're all very quiet. John Campbell was the great exception, because he wasn't a writer any more and had become an editor. He would talk to all his writers, and would give several of them the same idea and they would each handle it differently. In fact if you came in with one idea he would quite often talk you out of it, then give the idea to someone else that he thought might do a better job of it.

EVANS: You've written so much that it would be impossible to go into every story in detail. I'd be inclined to pick what I always think are your two most outstanding and characteristic works in science fiction – one is the 'Foundation' series and the other is the 'Robot' stories. Could we talk about the 'Foundation' series first of all? Did you realize when you started it that it had a great history ahead of it?

ASIMOV: Well now you won't be surprised, after what I've just said, if I tell you that 'Foundation' was a lot more John Campbell than myself. I came in one day with an idea for a short story about the fall of the galactic empire, and he turned that down flat. He said the idea was too big for a short story and that he wanted a whole new history. He wanted me to sit down and write the history as an outline and then build the stories around it. I refused to do that because writing the history would be extremely dull and I would never stick to it, but said I would be glad to try to write the first story of it and see how it went. So I went home and wrote a story called 'Foundation'. It was about 12,000 words long, a novelette really, and it dealt with a group of people on a world on the outskirts of the galaxy, trying to preserve human knowledge in the light of what seemed the obvious and inevitable fall of the galactic empire. I finished it in cliff-hanging fashion. In other words I did not reveal the solution to the difficulty that faced the people on that world but I had my hero say it was obvious, obvious as all hell. That's the way the story ended.

There had to be another story and it had to be in the next issue, which meant that I had one month to write it in, and after starting to write it I was very sorry because I was getting into difficulties and was afraid I wouldn't make it in time. I distinctly remember standing on a bridge between Brooklyn and Manhattan – I don't know which one – talking to Fred Pohl about this, and saying that I was caught in the dilemma. I simply had to have that story done in a week or so and I wasn't sure how to get out of it. Well he must have suggested something, because after that I went home and finished the story and it was sold as 'Bridle and Saddle' and did appear in the next issue. What it was that Fred suggested I swear I don't remember, but it must have been something, and something useful. After that there were no problems. Every once in a while John Campbell would say 'Isn't it time for another "Foundation" story?', and I'd sit down and write another one. Occasionally he would suggest an idea himself. For example, he suggested the notion of having Hari Seldon come back once in a while – which I objected to at first, and indeed dropped it after a while because I felt it was too artificial. Then he suggested the Mule, and I said that would upset the Seldon plan, and he said 'Good, I want you to upset it and to see what you do with that'. So, with a great deal of trepidation, I wrote 'The Mule', which was the longest story I had written up to that point. It was a two-part serial, the first time I'd written a serial, and I found I enjoyed it very much.

I continued for, I think, two more stories, each one longer than the one before, and then suddenly it just became too difficult to move. I had written about a quarter of a million words of 'Foundation' and each time I began a new story for the sake of those readers who hadn't read the previous ones, I had to briefly summarize what had gone before. It became more and more difficult to think up a natural device with which to do it – I had to have the people in the story explaining to each other what they all knew. It's as if every time you want to write a story about American history you have to have somebody explaining the American Revolution to someone who knows all about it. In the final story I resorted to the device of having my fourteen-year-old heroine writing a school essay in which her task was to describe the Seldon Plan, and so she did. I felt I just couldn't face it one more time, especially since each time I wrote another story everything had to be re-read to double-check for continuity – and even so there are people who now and again present me with three pages, single spaced, of various inconsistencies in the series. So I have not written any more.

The last story of the 'Foundation' series was written in 1949, published in 1950, and I've resisted all attempts (and they have been constant and inexorable) at making me continue the series. Don't forget the series only covers the first three hundred years of what was originally intended to be a thousand year history, so there's plenty of room to go further. But I wrote it in my twenties and I am now in my fifties, and am not the same person. I have other interests and I'm not sure I could do it. Furthermore, I'm afraid that if I try to write more 'Foundation' what will happen is everyone will tell everyone else 'Just read it up to this point, everything that comes afterwards is really no good'.

EVANS: I just detected a very slight note of hesitancy, or was I being optimistic? It sounded as though, somewhere in your mind, you were kicking round the notion that you might just conceivably do another bit of 'Foundation'.

ASIMOV: Well the pressure *has* increased, and Doubleday has sworn to me that if I write a fourth 'Foundation' book it could make me a lot of money and my readers would be very happy. The point is that the three 'Foundation' books have been like an annuity to me, they make more money than anything else I write, and they continue to make more money. They're never out of print, they sell in hard cover and in soft cover simultaneously; as a three-volume edition, as three one-volume editions, in paperback also. I mean it never stops and probably more people read and enjoy it than any other book of mine. So I wouldn't be human if I didn't feel that perhaps I ought to do more of it.

To tell you the truth I even started writing more 'Foundation' and wrote about ten pages – and it seemed like 'Foundation' all right. But unfortunately everyone's after me for something or other – it's really very distressing. When I first started writing copiously, when I quit teaching back in '58 and decided to be a full-time writer, I had a definite fear that I would out-write myself – either run out of subjects to write about or else start competing with myself and the publishers would refuse to publish too many of my books. Well it hasn't happened. I've written as much as I can – in the last sixty-five months I have published sixty-five books, so that for over five years now I've been saying to myself 'This just can't keep on.' But what *has* happened is that more and more publishers have been asking me for more and more books and I can never get down to some specific book that I would perhaps want to do, like the 'Foundation'. Maybe I use that as an excuse not to get on with the 'Foundation' because I don't really want to do it. At the present moment I'm working on six or seven books simultaneously and switch from one to the other. Maybe I've reached the point where the bubble is bursting because I don't know when I'll finish any of them.

EVANS: Most of your books at the moment are not science fiction at all, but what I'd describe as expert science fact and scientific popularization. One tends to forget that you actually began as a scientist and only gave up when you found that you could make so much out of writing. How useful do you feel your scientific background was – what has it really given your science fiction?

ASIMOV: Actually it's the other way round. I was originally a science fiction writer because I started writing science fiction professionally while in college. I wrote primarily to make tuition money to get through to become a scientist, and by the time I became a scientist (my Ph.D. in chemistry came in '48) I had already been a science fiction writer for ten years. I went to Boston University School of Medicine and to the Biochemistry Department. In 1955 I became an associate professor, but by 1958 it was obvious to me that my life was writing, nothing else. So I quit my job as a teacher, although retaining a professorial title. But one thing science has given my science fiction is that it allows me to write science fiction with greater authority – at least the kind of science fiction I like to write. It also gives me a kind of added respectability as a science fiction writer. To be just a science fiction writer is one thing; to be a science fiction writer who can also legitimately call himself a scientist is quite another. The distinction is a false one, but it exists. There's a certain snob appeal in being a scientist, and thus people will take you more seriously as a science fiction writer if you're a scientist. People feel that they can invite you to be on panels as a science fiction writer along with others who are primarily scientists, without disgracing the panel.

In a sense I became myself a kind of phenomenon because of the two hats I can wear, each reinforcing the other. Then as I wrote and discovered that I could write in a number of fields without making an absolute jack-ass of myself, I became yet another kind of phenomenon. It wasn't just a matter of being prolific, because I am not so prolific as, for instance, Erle Stanley Gardner, Edgar Wallace, Georges Simenon, John Creasey or people like that – but they only wrote mysteries. I write *everything* and that sort of intrigues people too. I now have published 168 books on, even to me, an incredible number of subjects. One of my recent books is called 'Lecherous Limericks' – there are a hundred limericks all made up by myself, all lecherous. And I have recently written a straight murder mystery. It's the first time I've ever written a murder mystery, with no SF aspect in it, no scientists in it, just plain straight mystery. I've also been working on a book in which I annotate a number of familiar poems, some of them not exactly great poems, like the 'Ride of Paul Revere' by Henry Wadsworth Longfellow. But in a sense I lead the best of all possible lives. I write easily and readily, knowing for a fact that I can get anything published, which means that writing is a total pleasure, never spoiled by the constant fear of 'Will this be acceptable?' I *never* think of that, I *know* it's acceptable.

EVANS: Could we just return to the 'Foundation' epic, and talk about the idea of psychohistory which featured strongly in it. To me it looks very much like the current quasi-science of futurology. What gave you the idea about psychohistory?

ASIMOV: Well that grew out of another talk with John Campbell. I should say that every once in a while I get letters from kids telling me that in reading the 'Foundation' series they detect a similarity to the *Fall of the Roman Empire*, and am I aware of it? Yes, I write back, I am, I modelled it on it. Very closely in fact, in particular the idea that on the galactic empire the outskirts would revert to barbarism. Now while talking to John about this decay in the outskirts, he said that perhaps there ought to be a special Foundation established way out in the sticks which would be working deliberately towards the reconstitution of the empire. I said, 'Well, how would they know what to do?' and he said perhaps someone had worked out a way of predicting the future on purely logical grounds, and from that the notion of Hari Seldon arose and also that of psychohistory. And so on, little by little. The whole series, you see, didn't spring from my mind in one great swoop – it developed. That was another reason why it was so difficult to write because I wrote each sequence of it (there was a total of nine separate stories) without any consideration of what was to come next. I was intent on making each particular story good and, of course, gradually wrote myself more and more into a corner. So much so that by the time the ninth story was finished it was becoming extremely difficult to decide what I could do next within the limits I had set myself in the previous stories.

Also, we have to remember that when I had finished the last story it was '49 and changes were coming over me. A new magazine came out called *Galaxy Science Fiction*, and then another new magazine called *Fantasy and Science Fiction*. I was on fire to try to write for these because I was very conscious of the fact that over a space of years I had written only for Campbell – even the stories that had appeared elsewhere were Campbell rejects – and I was dreadfully afraid that I was a one-man writer. My attempts to get into the other magazines meant that I had to write something other than 'Foundation', because 'Foundation' *was Astounding*. Also in January 1950 my first book, *Pebble in the Sky*, came out, and thereafter I was anxious to write science fiction novels with book rather than magazine publication in mind. Admittedly several of them were set in the 'Foundation' universe, but during the time when the galactic empire was still powerful. *Pebble in the Sky* itself was set at the time of the powerful galactic empire; *Occurrence in Space* and *Stars, Like Dust* at the time the galactic empire was being established; 'Caves of Steel' and *The Naked Sun* were written in a different universe, as was the *End of Eternity*. But you see, things began to vary with me, and 'Foundation' had been the major portion of my output for so many years that I eagerly went away from it in order to see if I could do something else.

EVANS: The other great theme that I always associate with you, is the *I Robot* series, and that concerns predictions of a future which is much closer to us than the 'Foundation'. Now, when you were writing that, we were in the very early days of computing science, and only the most advanced and ambitious computer scientists were thinking at all about the consequences of artificial intelligence. Yet obviously you had this sitting there in your heart.

ASIMOV: Yes, now you see this is an interesting point because one would think that I wrote the stories because I had some insight into computer technology and could see further than even the computer technologists themselves. Nothing could be further from the truth because when I first started writing my 'Robot' series, back in 1939, that was before Vanevar Bush had put up his first all-electronic computer. I had no knowledge whatsoever of computers, and I never did have until after the war, by which time the various 'Robot' stories and *I Robot* had all been written. Actually, they came not from anything that was done in science but from the previous history of science fiction. Robots had been a staple of earlier science fiction, but they had almost always been there in the form that had started with Mary Shelley's *Frankenstein*. The robot was a monster, a soulless piece of life which had been produced by a scientist who should never have done it. A scientist activated by hubris was defying the gods by taking over a god-like function, producing life, and was therefore fittingly punished when the robot turned against him and had to be destroyed. It's the Sorcerer's Apprentice again. I grew tired of that plot and felt that it would be an interesting thing if I could treat robots, not as examples of hubris, not as examples of scientists defying the gods, but just as engineering devices which like any other engineering devices, would have to have built-in safeguards. That was the important thing, the safeguards to prevent what I call the Frankenstein neurosis. And so after a while I crystallized this into the three laws of robotics. In the very first robot story I made reference to the fact that robots were built in such a way that they could not turn on their creators and could not harm human beings. But by the fourth story I had actually set down the three laws and they of course have been a staple of my stories ever since. There's a Robot story in a Ballantine anthology of originals called the 'Bicentennial Man', and it starts with the quotation of the three laws of robotics – I couldn't possibly write a robot story now without it. It is these three laws I think that made my robot stories different from any others, and in fact outlawed the old-fashioned robot stories from the pages of respectable science fiction. I suppose you can still find them in comic books and in cheap movies, but anyone who writes science fiction seriously cannot write a robot story without at least implicit acceptance of the three laws.

EVANS: We'd better state the three laws I think.

ASIMOV: Okay, the first law is this: a robot may not harm a human being or through inaction allow a human being to come to harm. The second law is that a robot must obey the orders given it by human beings, except when such orders would conflict with the first law. The third law is that a robot must protect its own existence, except where that would conflict with the first or second laws.

EVANS: And the *I Robot* stories were really permutations of the difficulties that might arise in real-life situations where robots were forced into juggling the respective merits of these laws.

ASIMOV: Yes, the laws are sufficiently ambiguous so that you can consider ways in which the laws won't necessarily cope with the real things. At the start I began with rather trivial difficulties arising, but as time went on I was more or less forced into a deeper philosophic consideration of what the laws meant. Of course in the very beginning I realized that there was one particular rock on which these three laws could founder if one was to push it. That is, 'What is a man?' In other words, what is this thing that a robot mustn't harm and that a robot must obey? How does one know for sure a man is not a robot, or even a robot is not a man? Now I didn't take this puzzle up, not because I didn't think it was important, but because I wasn't sure what I ought to do with it. Then recently, when asked by the editor of *Fantasy and Science Fiction* to write what I considered to be the ultimate robot story, I figured the only way to do that would be to take up the question of 'What is man?' So I wrote a story called 'That Thou Art Mindful of Him' (because that, of course, is the rest of the quotation 'What is man that thou art mindful of him ...?'). In this story the robots have to face the fact that after a certain point, since they become intellectually superior to man, they must define man not as a particular biological species but as *the dominant* intellectual form on Earth – which then becomes themselves.

EVANS: This is tremendously topical really because of the current scientific research into the field of artificial intelligence. Although it's been moving very slowly, there really is more and more effort being put into it, and as computers get smarter and smarter and smarter, it seems to me that at some stage in the game – I don't know when it will be, ten, twenty, thirty or forty years, it's irrelevant really – we'll need to be considering and acting out all the possibilities that you were talking about in the *I Robot* series.

ASIMOV: Yes, it sometimes seems to me that if there is a future and if I am remembered in it, it may well be for having established the base for the society of that time. Because I do feel that when robots actually come into existence something very much like the three laws will *have* to exist. As a matter of fact, somebody wrote an article a few years back in an architectural journal in which he pointed out that the three laws actually govern tools in general and are already implemented. All we have to do is to rephrase the three laws as follows: By the first law a tool must be safe to use; by the second law a tool must fulfil the function for which it is intended – as long as it is safe. And for the third law a tool must endure as long as it possibly can, provided that this doesn't violate either of the first two laws. Perhaps when the three laws of robotics are established it will be known as 'Asimov's three laws of robotics' – well it's nice to think of!

EVANS: Do you feel that current developments in artificial intelligence, leading possibly to a computer which could have some bit of self-consciousness, is likely to affect man's image of himself?

ASIMOV: Well I suppose man will resent this and there will be a strong effort, which may win out, not to produce computers that are rivals to man, or to destroy any that are produced. I feel myself to be in a rather tiny minority in this respect. So far evolution has come along through hit-and-miss, random processes, and perhaps once you achieve a species which is intelligent enough to guide evolution, then the old random, hit-and-miss methods are no longer efficient. In other words, from this point on we should expect mankind to guide evolution, both of his own and of other species. An 'artificial intelligence' is of course another species, and perhaps if we can more rapidly produce an artificial brain superior to the ordinary human brain, then that is the direction that evolution ought to go, regardless of our personal feelings. It doesn't matter to us that the reptiles probably disapproved of being replaced by the mammals, or that the mammals themselves probably disapproved of having the primates take over the leadership. All life forms perhaps, if they had the vote, would disapprove of mankind dominating. We don't care about such disapproval. We feel that evolution ought to progress in the direction that it does, as long as *we* are the end-product. Well by the same argument, there's nothing sacred about us either, and there's no reason why an intelligent computer, an artificial intelligence superior to our own, should not succeed to the 'domination of the world' in the same way that we have already done. In fact, considering what we are doing to the world right now, my own feeling is that it's a shame that we can't get the intelligent robots to take over faster than they are likely to, so that they can save the earth.

By the way, this puts me in mind of one of my own short stories – my personal favourite in fact – written back in 1956, called 'The Last Question'. It is my favourite because of all my stories this was the one in which I allowed my imagination to run most riot, and to dip into the future as far as the human mind could reach. I have included it in two or three of my own collections; oddly enough it hasn't been much anthologized, so perhaps not everybody views it as I do. But I don't care.

It's really a description, in six scenes, of the next trillion years in human history, showing the parallel development of human beings and computers. It shows, at each stage, how humanity makes enormous strides, from developing use of direct solar energy, to developing interstellar travel, to developing immortality, to developing the ability to live outside bodies, and so on. At the same time computers become more and more advanced, more and more capable, more and more existent in hyperspace, more and more able to be everywhere in the universe. Finally they get so intelligent and capable that all you've got to do is to ask them a question and the super-computer answers. Until finally the universe dies, even though all through this history there has been this continual question arising – hence 'The Last Question' as the title – as to whether there is any way of reversing the inevitable death of the universe. Once entropy reaches its maximum, disorder reaches its maximum, everything evens out. There are no more stars, no more energy available for use. Is there any way of winding it all up again, turning it up, reversing the process? In the end all that exists is the computer in hyperspace and the last human souls are somehow made one with the computer, and then the computer hovers over the dead universe to decide what it can do about it. Finally it figures out how to restore everything. And the computer says 'Let there be light', and there was light.

EVANS: Yes, that's a marvellous idea, and exactly what you set out to write – the ultimate computer story. Could I ask you now about your favourite science fiction story, short or long, written by a writer other than yourself?

ASIMOV: Well I must give a double answer there, because my favourite story could be either the one that impressed me most at the time I first read it, or the story that looking back I *now* realize was the best I ever read. Well the one that affected me most, the one that came along and hit me just at the time I was ready to be hit, was 'Galactic Patrol' by E. E. Smith. It was published in 1938, I was eighteen years old and I just loved it. I don't recall ever having so exalted a feeling as a result of reading anything as I did in reading the first of the six parts of 'Galactic Patrol'. And yet when, many years later, I tried to pick it up again, I found that it was quite unreadable. Now another story which affected me very much at the time, very much, was also a 1938 story – it was 'Who Goes There?' by John Campbell. It didn't hit me as hard as 'Galactic Patrol' had done, but on re-reading it, quite recently, I found that it held up exceedingly well and that I was still mightily impressed by it. And so for me 'Who Goes There?' by John Campbell is the greatest science fiction story I've ever read. On the other hand, my favourite author is Arthur Clarke, and I suppose in a way this is just a variation of the truth that my favourite author is *really* myself. Because of all the science fiction writers the writer whose work is most nearly like mine in spirit is Arthur Clarke's. In fact I can bet you that anybody who likes what I write likes Arthur Clarke's books too, and vice versa. And that anyone who doesn't like me doesn't like Arthur, and vice versa. We are the Bobsy twins of science fiction.

EVANS: The kind of question that people always ask, and it is a useful question to ask, is about the significance of science fiction. Whether in the long run it is anything more than superior entertainment using the concepts of one particular time, in the way that, say, the Westerns used the concepts of one era and historical novels use the concepts of another. What do you feel, in the long run, is the real significance of science fiction?

ASIMOV: Well let's look at it this way: science fiction deals, to my way of thinking, with the response of human beings to changes in the level of science and technology. It is the only form of literature which routinely deals with *change*, which assumes that the society of the future will be different from the society of today. The difference may be for the better or for the worse, or the words better and worse may not have meanings, but it will be *different*. Now this is important because there is no other form of literature that deals with change. In ancient times, or even in relatively recent times, when people wrote about the future there was no real notion of change. Any society was just like the present one. But science fiction, ever since the time of, I would suppose, Edgar Allen Poe, accepts change, because something new happened in the nineteenth century.

Of course throughout history society changed as the result of technological change. For example you discover fire, you develop agriculture, you begin to herd animals, you develop the printing press, you discover the magnetic compass – all these produced profound changes, but so slowly that in a single lifetime any individual human wouldn't notice it – he'd think things were always the same. It was only with the establishment of the Industrial Revolution in Great Britain towards the end of the eighteenth century and the beginning of the nineteenth, that for the first time the rate of change of society became fast enough for an individual to observe it *in his own lifetime*. And that meant the birth of a new curiosity, because until then people hadn't really worried about what the future would be like. If they lived a long and happy life they closed their eyes in peace and contentment: they had seen it *all*. But, at the beginning of the nineteenth century, it was possible for people to die with a raging curiosity not satisfied – what would things be like after they were dead, in the time of their grandchildren and great-grandchildren? They knew it would be different from what they had seen – it might even be startlingly different. This brand new curiosity had never existed on earth before, and in order to fulfil it, people tried to imagine what the future might be like. Therefore true science fiction only became possible after the Industrial Revolution.

Now the important thing is that the rate of change has continued to increase, and today we are living at a time when mankind is in a state of deep, deep trouble. Unless we can somehow anticipate the changes to come and order our lives in such a way that we can take advantage of these changes for the good of man, and not allow it to work for the bad of man, we are simply not going to survive. It's for this reason that I think that science fiction is important because it is the *only* form of literature which gets people accustomed to the inevitability of change. I think that all futurists, or at least those who are any good at all, have at sometime in their life been interested in science fiction, may have even tried to write science fiction. I do not think it is possible that anyone can be truly interested in the future and never have been interested in science fiction.

Furthermore, science fiction acts as a way of trying on or testing out different futures, seeing what you like and don't like about them. *1984* I think has permanently fixed in many people a dislike of a big-brother-type of future. It may turn out that the big-brother-type of future is something that is necessary, but if it comes it will have to override the dislike that was originated through *1984*. On the other hand, H. G. Wells and his pictures of the future somehow made many people *like* the idea of a technological future, and this brings about a certain mental fix as well.

Now with all this in mind, people frequently ask whether I am personally optimistic or pessimistic about the future. Personally I am pessimistic. The rate of change has increased so fast and the technological capacity of man has so vastly outstripped his social awareness, so to speak, that I don't think the gulf can be bridged in time to save us. For example, I don't believe we can persuade humanity to end the population explosion fast enough to keep that explosion from killing us. At the present rate of population increase there are going to be seven billion of us by the year 2000. I don't believe we can support seven billion by the year 2000, and fear therefore that we are on the edge of the great famines. That the breakdown of our technological civilization may well follow the social dislocations of these famines. The economic interdependence of the various portions of the earth has reached the level now where if we have a *real* dislocation anywhere on earth it affects all the rest of earth, and if half of the earth begins to starve to death I do not think the other half can remain untouched. So I do not expect we will be able to avoid catastrophe, and to that extent I am pessimistic.

Now the next question is, can we survive the catastrophe? In other words, after enough people die will the remainder be able to continue civilization on perhaps a wiser path? This I am less pessimistic about, but not really entirely optimistic either. Because in these last decades of the twentieth century, as the catastrophe hits, I very much fear that we may burn up all our oil, burn up the most easily available coal, spread our minerals thin, perhaps even in desperation have a nuclear war – I don't know. We may end up simply without a sufficient energy base to keep civilization going. However, I expect I won't live to see the final decision, and am in a way really rather glad of that. I am not sufficiently confident that the final decision will be in our favour to want to live to see it. But I think anybody today who's thirty years old, or younger, will live to see the final decision made. I'm talking of course about the decision as to whether our society will continue, perhaps into the indefinite future, once the present serious problems are solved, or whether in actual fact this is the final century of our industrial civilization.

Small World

Bob Shaw

I'll do it today, Robbie thought. *I'll run across the sky today.*
He drew the bed-clothes more closely around him, creating
a warm cave which was precisely tailored to his small frame,
and tried to go back to sleep. It was not yet morning and the
house was quiet except for occasional murmurs from the
refrigerator in the kitchen. Robbie found, however, that
making the decision about the sky run had changed his mood,
permitted the big and hazardous outside world to invade his
security, and that sleep was no longer possible. He got up,
went to the window and drew the curtains aside.

The three mirrors which captured sunlight had not yet
been splayed out from the sides of the cylindrical space colony,
and therefore it was still completely dark outside the house
except for the luminance from the streetlamps. The nearby
rooftops were silhouetted against the horizontal strip of
blackness, unrelieved by stars, which Robbie knew as the
night-time sky, but higher up he could see the glowing
geometrical patterns of streets in the next valley. He stared
at the jewelled rectangles and pretended he was a bird soaring
above them in the night air. The game occupied his mind
for only a short time – he had never seen a real bird, and his
imagination was not fully able to cope with the old earth-
bound concepts of 'above' and 'below'. Robbie closed the
drapes, went back to bed and waited impatiently for morning . . .

'Come on, Robbie,' his mother called. 'It's time for breakfast.'

He sat up with a jerk, amazed to discover that he had,
after all, been able to doze off and return to the peaceful
world of dreams after the pledge he had made to himself.

All the while he was washing and dressing he tried to get accustomed to the idea that this was the day on which he was going to grow up, to become a full member of the Red Hammers. His mind was still swirling with the sense of novelty and danger when he went into the bright kitchen and took his place in the breakfast alcove opposite his father and mother.

Like most colonists who had managed to settle happily on Island One, they were neat, medium-sized, unremarkable people of the sort who leave their youth behind very quickly, but are compensated with a seemingly endless span of un-changing adulthood. Mr Tullis was a crystallogenetic engineer in the zero-gravity workshops at the centre of the Island's sunward cap – an occupation which was beyond Robbie's comprehension; and Mrs Tullis was a psychologist specializing in verbal communication modes – an occupation Robbie might have understood had she ever talked to him about it. They both examined him critically as he sat down.

'What are you going to do today?' his mother said, handing him a dish of cereal.

'Nothin'.' Robbie stared down at the yellow feathers of grain, and he thought, *I'm going to run across the sky.*

'Noth*ing*,' she repeated, emphasizing the ending for Robbie's benefit. 'That doesn't sound very constructive.'

'The school holidays are too long.' Max Tullis stood up and reached for his jacket. 'I'm going to be late at the plant.'

Thea Tullis stood up with him and accompanied him to the front door while they discussed arrangements for a dinner party that evening. On her return she busied herself for a few minutes disposing of the breakfast remains and, her interest in Robbie's plans apparently having faded, disappeared without speaking into the room she used as a study. Robbie toyed with his cereal, then drank the chill, malty-flavoured milk from the dish. He looked around the kitchen for a moment, suddenly reluctant to go outside and face the rest of the day, but he had discovered that when his mother was working in her study the house was lonelier than when he was the only person in it. Taking some candy from a dish on the window ledge, he opened the door and went out to the back garden.

Robbie often watched television programmes which were beamed out from Earth, and so had a fairly clear mental image of how a natural environment should look, but there was no sense of dislocation in his mind as he glanced around him on a quiet, summer morning. He had been born on Island One and saw nothing out of the ordinary about living on the inner surface of a glass-and-metal cylinder little more than two hundred metres in diameter and a kilometre in length. The colony was highly industrialized – because it manufactured many of the components for larger second-generation space habitats – but it had a residential belt supporting over a thousand families. This community, with a fourteen-year history of living in space, yielded valuable sociological data and therefore was preserved intact, even though its members could have been moved on to newer colonies.

None of Robbie's friends were visible in the row of adjoining gardens, so he emitted a sharp, triple-toned whistle, a secret signal devised by the Red Hammers, and sat down on a rustic seat to await results. Several minutes went by without an answering whistle being heard. Robbie was not particularly surprised. He had noticed that – no matter how strict the injunctions were from their leaders at night – the Hammers tended to sleep late in the morning during school holidays. On this occasion, though, he was disappointed at their tardiness because he anticipated the looks of respect from the other junior members when he announced he was taking his initiation.

He munched candy for a few minutes, then boredom began to set in and he thought about asking his mother to take him to the low-gravity park in the Island's outer cap. She had refused similar requests twice already that week, and he guessed her reply would be the same today. Dismissing the idea from his mind, he lay back in the chair and stared upwards, focusing his gaze on the houses and gardens visible 'above' him in the Blue Valley. The layout of the residential areas was identical in all three valleys, and Robbie was able to pick out the counterpart of his own family's house in the Blue Valley and – by looking back over his shoulder – in the

Yellow Valley. At that time there was a temporary truce between the Red Hammers and the Yellow Knives, so Robbie's attention was concentrated on enemy territory, that inhabited by the Blue Flashes. He had memorized the map drawn up by his own gang, and as a result was able to pick out the actual houses where the Blue Flash leaders lived.

As the minutes stretched out his boredom and restlessness increased. He stood up and gave the secret whistle again, making it louder this time. When there was no response he paced around the garden twice, making sure that no adults were watching him from windows of neighbouring houses, then slipped into the cool privacy of the shrubs at the foot of the lawn. A sense of guilty pleasure grew within him as he scooped up some of the crumbly soil with his hands and uncovered a small object wrapped in plastic film. Catapults were illegal on Island One – as were firearms and all explosive devices which might be capable of puncturing the pressure skin – but most boys knew about catapults, and some claimed the historic privilege of making them, regardless of any authority.

Robbie tested the strength of the synthetic rubber strands, enjoying the feeling of power the simple weapon gave him, and took a projectile from his pocket. There were no pebbles in the sieved and sterilized soil of the Island, but he made it a practice to collect suitably small and heavy objects. This one was a glass stopper from an old whisky decanter, almost certainly stolen, which he had bought from a girl in school. He fitted it into the catapult's leatherette cup, drew the rubber back to full stretch, and – after a final check that he was not being observed – fired it upwards in the general direction of the residential area of the Blue Valley.

The glass missile glittered briefly in the sunlight, and vanished from sight.

Robbie watched its disappearance with a feeling of deep satisfaction. His pleasure was derived from the fact that he had defied, and somehow revenged himself upon, his parents and all the other adults who either ignored him or placed meaningless restrictions on his life. He also had a ten-year-old boy's faith that Providence would guide the projectile to land squarely on the roof of the gang hut used by the despicable Blue Flashes. His mind was filled with a gleeful vision of one of their full-scale meetings being thrown into panic and disorder by the thunderous impact just above their heads.

A moment later he heard an elaborate whistle coming from one of the nearby gardens and he lost all interest in the now invisible missile. He wrapped up the catapult, buried it, and ran to meet his friends.

The glass stopper which Robbie had dispatched into the sky weighed some sixty grammes and had he lived on Earth it would have travelled only a short distance into the air before falling back. Island One rotated about its longitudinal axis once every twenty-one seconds, thus creating at the inner surface an apparent gravity equal to that of Earth at sea level. The gradient was on an entirely different scale to that of Earth, however – falling from maximum to zero in a distance of only a hundred metres, which was the radius of the cylindrical structure.

In the early stages of its flight the gleaming missile decelerated in much the same manner as it would have done while rising from the surface of a planet, but the forces retarding it quickly waned, allowing its ascent to be prolonged. It actually had some residual velocity when it reached the zero-gravity zone of the axis and, describing a sweeping S-curve, plunged downwards into the Blue Valley.

And, because the space colony had rotated considerably during its time of flight, the stopper landed nowhere near Robbie's notional target.

Alice Ledane was lying in a darkened room at the front of her house, hands clasped to her temples, when she heard the explosive shattering of the window which overlooked the rear patio.

She lay still for a pounding moment, rigid with shock, while her heart lurched and thudded like an engine shuddering to a halt. For what seemed a long time she was positive she was going to die, but her shallow, ultra-rapid fear-breathing gradually steadied into a more normal rhythm. She got to her feet and, leaning against the wall at intervals, went towards the back of the house. The mood of calmness and resolve she had been trying to nurture had gone, and for a moment she was afraid to open the door of the living-room. When she finally did so her lips began to quiver as the remnants of her selfcontrol dwindled away.

Shards of glass were scattered around the room like transparent petals, some of them hanging by their points from the drapes, and ornaments had been toppled from the small table which sat at the window. The surface of the table was dented, but she could see nothing of the missile which must have been thrown from the back garden. Alice gazed at the damage, knuckles pressed to her mouth, then she ran to the back door and threw it open. As she had expected, there was no sign of the children who for months had been persecuting her with such unyielding determination.

'Damn you!' she shouted. 'It isn't fair! What have I done to you? Why don't you come out in the open?'

There was a lengthy silence, disturbed only by the humming of bees in the hedgerows, then the tall figure of Mr Chuikov appeared at an upper window of the next house. Alice slammed her door, suddenly afraid of being seen, and stumbled back to the front room where she had been resting. She went to the sideboard, picked up a framed photograph of her husband, and stared at the unperturbed, smiling face.

'And damn you, Victor,' she said. 'You'd no right! No . . . bloody . . . *right*!'

While she was looking at the photograph, her hand made its own way into the pocket of her dressing-gown and emerged holding a strip of bubbled tinfoil. Alice put the picture down and ejected a silver-and-blue capsule from the strip. She raised the tiny ovoid to her mouth, but hesitated without swallowing it. For the past week – in accordance with Dr Kinley's suggestion – she had progressively delayed the taking of the first cap by an extra hour every day. The aim, the shining goal, was to get through an entire day without any

psychotropic medication at all. If that could be achieved just
once there would be prospects of further successes and of
finally becoming a whole woman again.

Alice rolled the capsule between her finger and thumb, and
knew this was not to be her day of triumph – the children
had seen to that. Harold from three doors along the block,
or Jean from the house on the corner, or Carl from the next
street. With the casual ruthlessness of the very young they
had long ago deduced that her illness made her an easy prey,
and they had declared a quiet war. Alice placed the capsule on
her tongue, yielding to its promise of a few hours of peace,
then an irksome thought occurred to her. While she was
asleep the broken window in the living room would admit
dust, insects, possibly even human intruders. There had once
been a time when she could have slept contentedly in an
unlocked house, but the world and all the people in it had been
different then.

She took the capsule from her mouth, dropped it into her
pocket, and went to fetch a waste bin. It took her fifteen
minutes to gather up the larger fragments of glass, an armoury
of brittle daggers, and to vacuum the carpet until it was free
of gleaming splinters. The next logical step would have been
to contact the maintenance department and report the damage,
but she had had the telephone disconnected a year previously
because its unexpected ringing had jolted her nerves too much.
She had even, and quite illegally, cut the wires of the public
service loudspeaker in the hall for the same reason. On this
occasion it would not have taken long to get dressed and go to
a phone in the shopping arcade, but Alice shrank from the
idea of leaving the security of the house at such short notice.
Her only option was to cover the broken window in some way
until she felt strong enough to have it properly mended.

In the spare bedroom, the one Victor had used as a workshop, she found a sheet of alloy wide enough to span the
window, and a quick search along the shelves produced a
tube of Liqueld adhesive. She carried the materials into the
living room, squeezed some adhesive onto the metal window
frame and pressed the alloy into position. Within a minute

it was so firmly in place that it was beyond her strength to move it. Satisfied that her defences were once again intact, Alice closed up the drapes, returned to the front room and lay down on the divan. The rolls of fat which had gathered around her body in a year of housebound inactivity had hampered her in the work she had just done and she was breathing heavily. The acrid smell of unhealthy perspiration filled the room.

'Damn you, Victor,' she said to the ceiling. 'You'd no right.'

Victor Ledane had been one of a team of five who had gone outside the sunward cap of a Model Two habitat to install a parabolic mirror which was going to be used as an auxiliary power source. The work was being done in a hurry against a completion deadline imposed by engineer-politicians back on Earth. As Alice understood it, one of the team had ignored standard procedure and had begun stripping the non-reflective coating from the dish before it was fully secured. Only a fraction of the bright metal surface had been uncovered, but when the mirror accidentally swung free of its mountings a blade of solar heat had sliced open the space suits of two men. And one of them had been Victor Ledane.

Alice and he had been living on Island One for six years at the time. Those had been good years, so absorbing that she had lost contact with her few friends back on Earth, and when the Island's community director, Les Jerome, had asked her to stay on she had readily agreed. She had known, of course, that the sociologists and psychologists were mainly interested in having a genuine space widow on tap, but with Victor gone nothing seemed very important. Obligingly, she had continued to live in the same house, had waited for the promised return of joy, and had tried not to think about the hard vacuum of space which began centimetres beneath the floor.

The trouble was . . . there had been no resurgence of joy.

Eventually she had settled for an inferior substitute, one which was dispensed in the form of silver-and-blue capsules, and now it was becoming impossible to distinguish between the two. The only way to restore her judgement would be to start living without the capsules, getting through one week at a time, but the point that Dr Kinley and the others seemed to miss was that – to begin with – it would be necessary to get through that first, endless, impossible day ...

Alice fought to hold back the tears of frustration and despair as she realized that, on a day which had begun so disastrously, she was unlikely to hold on as late as noon before seeking relief. It came to her with a rare clarity that, for some people, the burdens of humanity were, quite simply, too great.

There was a gratifying response to Robbie's announcement.

After initial whoops of disbelief the younger members of the Red Hammers lapsed into silence, and Robbie could tell that – already – they were a little afraid of him. He made himself appear calm as Gordon Webb and the three other boys who made up the Supreme Council took him aside for a talk. Robbie went with them, occasionally glancing back at the juniors, and was thrilled to find that David, Pierre and Drew – even Gordon himself – were treating him almost as an equal. They were holding something in reserve, because he had not yet actually made the run, but Robbie was being given a strong foretaste of what it would be like to be a grown-up, and he found it a satisfying concoction. He wondered if his parents would notice a change in him when he went home for his evening meal, and if they would speculate on what had brought it about ...

'. . . make up your mind which valley you're going to,' Gordon was saying. 'Yellow or Blue?'

Robbie forced his thoughts back to the present, and to the unfortunate necessity of having to qualify for senior status in the gang. Because of the truce with the Yellow Knives there would be less risk in going in their direction, but there would be more glory in a fleeting invasion of Blue Flash territory, and it was the glory that Robbie wanted. The glory, the respect and the recognition.

'Blue,' he said, and then, remembering a line from a television drama, 'Where else?'

'Good man.' Gordon clapped him on the back. 'The Flashers are going to be sick. We'll show 'em.'

'We'd better get Robbie's challenge ready,' Drew said.

Gordon nodded. 'Are there any of the Blues watching us?'

Pierre took a small telescope from his pocket, moved out from the shade of the rhododendrons and trained the instrument on the Blue Valley residential section which was visible, at an altitude of some sixty degrees, above a strip of sky in which the Earth and Moon could be seen sweeping by every twenty-one seconds. As the distance from where the boys stood to the heart of Blue Flash territory was less than two hundred metres for the most part, the telescope was scarcely necessary, but it was a prestigious part of the Supreme Council's equipment and was always brought into action on such occasions.

'All clear,' Pierre droned presently, and Robbie felt a thrill at being at the centre of such military efficiency.

Gordon cupped his hands around his mouth and shouted instructions to the watchful group of juniors. 'Spread out and keep away from here. Create a diversion.'

The smaller boys nodded dutifully and moved away through the neat little park in the direction of their homes. Robbie was disappointed that they would not be present to see him make his run, but he understood the wisdom of Gordon's precautions. In addition to the risk of alerting the Blue Flashes, there was the more immediate danger of attracting the attention of adults in their own valley.

He went with the Council members to David's home, which was conveniently empty because both his parents were out at work, and they spent some time preparing his challenge. This was a large sheet of paper which he decorated with crossed hammers drawn in red ink. Across the bottom of the sheet, in elaborate lettering which was meant to look like Gothic script, Robbie printed the message: SIR ROBBIE TULLIS, GENTLEMAN SOLDIER OF THE RED HAMMERS, PRESENTS HIS COMPLIMENTS. When the ink had dried, the paper was folded up and tucked into an empty pickle jar, and – as the ultimate insult to the Blue Flashes – a scrap of red cloth was tied around it.

The task was more time-consuming than Robbie had expected and had barely been completed when the daycare matron for the area arrived to give David his lunch. This was the signal for the other boys to suspend operations and disperse to their own homes. Robbie was not hungry, but he went home as usual to avoid giving the impression that anything out of the ordinary was happening. He decided to preserve an enigmatic silence during the meal and, as his mother's thoughts were occupied with her morning's work, there was virtually no conversation. The house was filled with a cool stillness which seemed as though it might go on for ever.

It was with a sense of relief that Robbie finished eating and returned to the sunlit world of comradeship and conspiracy he shared with the other boys of the neighbourhood. Gordon, David, Pierre and Drew were waiting for him in a corner of the park, and as soon as he came near he knew by the solemnity of their faces that something had happened. Pierre, the tallest of the group, was anxiously scanning the vicinity, every now and then pausing to examine some item of suspicion with his telescope.

'Ole Minty saw us,' Gordon explained to Robbie. 'I think he's following us around.'

'Does that mean I can't . . .'

'No chance!' Gordon's twelve-year-old face showed the determination which had made him leader of the Red Hammers. 'We'll wear the old scarecrow down. Come on.'

Robbie tightened his grip on his challenge, which was hidden in the pocket of his jacket, and hurried after Gordon. He was impressed by the way in which the older boy seemed absolutely unafraid of one of the gang's most powerful enemies. Mr Mintoff was the Red Valley's first and only old age pensioner. Robbie knew he must have been a brilliant man to have been allowed to emigrate to Island One in his late middle age, but now he was a solitary figure with little to do except patrol the neighbourhood and act as unofficial policeman. In spite of the fact that he appeared to be senile, and walked with the aid of an alloy stick, he had the knack of divining what was going on in the Hammers' minds and of making sudden appearances at the most inopportune times.

Under Gordon's control, the group walked to the end of Centre Street and stood in a conspicuous knot, giving every indication they were planning mischief, until they saw Mr Mintoff approaching from the direction of the park. They let him get close, then split up and made their way by separate and secret routes to the opposite end of the street, where they again assembled. A good twenty minutes passed before the stooped form of Mr Mintoff caught up with them. Just before he was within hailing distance they disappeared as before, melting into the ample shrubbery of the Red Valley, and came together at their original venue to await their pursuer. The second round of the fight had got under way.

Robbie had been certain that Ole Minty would be forced to concede defeat within the hour, but he displayed a stubborn tenacity, and it was quite late in the afternoon before they saw him give up and turn into the side avenue where he lived. They waited a while longer to establish that they were in the clear, and Robbie's heart began to pick up speed as he realized that all the preliminaries had ended, that it was time for him to make his run . . .

The sidewall of the valley was constructed of smooth, seamless alloy and had a curved overhang which was supposed to make it unclimbable. Island One was an artificial environment, however, and as such it relied on complex engineering systems to maintain its various functions. The systems were designed to be as unobtrusive as possible, and most colonists were quite unaware of them, but children have an intense, detailed awareness of their surroundings, one which often confounds adult minds. Robbie and his four companions went straight to a point where a cluster of hydraulic pipes and valves made it easy to get halfway up the wall, and where a strain monitor installed by a different team of engineers provided a useful handhold at the top. He knew that if he stopped to think about what he was doing his nerve could fail, so he scaled the wall without hesitation and quickly slid onto the outer girder, where he could not be seen by anybody in his own valley. Making sure that his challenge was secure in his pocket, he turned to climb down to the surface of glass stretching away beneath.

And the universe made ready to swallow him.

Robbie froze, his muscles locked by fear, as he looked into the vertiginous deeps of space. The vast, curved window which separated two of the Island's valleys was like a tank filled with black liquid, a medium through which darted stars, planets, the blue Earth, the Moon, seemingly miniature models of other habitats – all of them impelled by the rotation of his own world. The huge plane mirror a short distance beyond the glass did nothing to lessen the fearful visual impact – it created discontinuities, a sense of depths within depths, as bright objects appeared and disappeared at its edges. Adding to the kaleidoscope of confusion were the sweeping, brilliant visions of Island One's sister cylinder, its own mirrors splayed out, which periodically drenched Robbie with upflung showers of white light.

He shrank back from the abyss, fighting to draw breath, face contorted with shock. Something in his pocket clinked against the metal of the girder. Robbie looked down at it, saw the top of the pickle jar containing his challenge, and moaned aloud as he realized he was not free to turn back. He lowered himself to the bottom flange of the girder, stepped out onto the nearly invisible surface of the glass, and began his run across the sky.

The wall of the Blue Valley was less than a hundred metres away, but as Robbie sprinted over the void it seemed to retreat, maliciously, prolonging his ordeal. Each leap over a titanium astragal brought with it a nightmarish moment of conviction that there would be nothing to land on at the other side, and that he would fall screaming into the endless night. And as he neared the midpoint of his run Robbie encountered a new and even more disconcerting phenomenon – the sun had appeared directly beneath his feet. Its reflected light blazed upwards around Robbie, blinding him and producing a nauseating sense of dislocation. He kept on running, but he had begun to sob painfully with each breath and attacks of dizziness threatened to bring him down.

All at once, the wall of the Blue Valley was looming up in front, criss-crossed by the shadows of a lattice girder. He pulled the glass jar from his pocket, hurled it over the wall and turned to run homewards on legs which had lost all strength.

Robbie made it to the centre of the window, to the centre of the fountain of golden fire, before he collapsed. He lay on his side, eyes tight-closed, knees pulled up to his chin, his immature personality in full flight from the world beyond the womb.

'Hold on a moment, Mr Mintoff.' Les Jerome set the telephone on his desk, picked up his binoculars and went to the window. From his office high up on the outer cap of Island One he could see virtually the entire structure of the colony. The opposite cap was at the centre of his field of view, and radiating from it were the three inhabited valleys interspersed with three, kilometre-long, transparencies. He aimed the powerful glasses at the strip between the Red and Blue Valleys, stood perfectly still for a moment, then picked up the phone.

'I see him, Mr Mintoff,' he said. 'Right beside Frame Thirty-two. Okay, you contact his mother. And thanks for calling – we'll get the little beggar in from there in a hurry.'

Jerome replaced the telephone and depressed the intercom toggle which would let him speak to the chief of his maintenance force. 'Frank, there's a kid stuck out on the glass. Yeah, on Transparency One just beyond Frame Thirty-two. Send somebody out to get him, and make sure a medic goes as well – the brat's going to need a shot of something to calm him down.'

Returning to the window, Jerome leaned on the ledge and stared at the strange, confined world he had grown to love in spite of all its faults and peculiarities. He had a decision to make, and it had to be done quickly. Strictly speaking, the plight of the boy out there on the glass did not constitute an emergency situation, and therefore he would not be officially justified in closing up the mirrors before the scheduled hour. All three mirrors had to be retracted at the same time to preserve the Island's symmetrical dynamics, which meant enforcing a universal black-out – and there were many colonists who objected strenuously to that sort of thing. There would be a barrage of complaints, some of them from influential people, but Jerome was a kindly man with two children of his own, and it troubled him to think of a small boy trapped on the glass, suspended in space.

The sooner he could put a semblance of solidity beneath the boy's feet and screen him off from infinity, the better chance the young adventurer would have of emerging from his ordeal without personality scars. He picked up the rarely-used red telephone which would transmit his voice to every home, office and workshop on Island One.

'This is Community Director Jerome speaking,' he said. 'There is no cause for alarm, but we are going to close up the mirrors for a short period. The black-out will be as brief as we can possibly make it, and I repeat there is no cause for alarm. I apologize for any inconvenience that may be caused. Thank you.'

Jerome then contacted his Engineering Executive and gave the order which would bring a premature sunset to his domain.

In the darkened front room of her house, midway along the Blue Valley, Alice Ledane awoke with a start.

She had been skimming on the wavetops of consciousness for hours, sometimes dipping into restless sleep as her private struggle drained her of nervous energy, then surfacing again to feel more exhausted than ever. As was usual on a day like this, she had no idea of the time. She got to her feet, parted the drapes slightly and made the discovery that it was night outside.

Incredulously, she put her hand in the pocket of her dressing-gown and found the day's first capsule still there. It was sticky to the touch. She held the tiny ovoid in the palm of her hand for a few seconds, then let it fall to the floor.

Alice went back to the divan and lay down. It was much too soon, she knew, to start congratulating herself on a victory – but if she had managed to get through one day with no outside help there was nothing to prevent her getting through the others which were to follow. Nothing insurmountable, anyway . . .

The sleep which came to her almost immediately was deep and dreamless and long-lasting, in contrast to her previous shallow dozing. It was the kind of sleep which all of life's warriors need to gird them for the morning and the bright light of the sun.

The Skytank Portfolio

Chris Boyce

This is the fifth time I have started writing this article and it is driving me out of my mind.

Who the hell wants to know about habitats apart from the space freaks and they know all I know anyway? Preaching to the converted. Bloody coals to Newcastle. The whole thing seems pointless.

Now that that is understood I am going to have an agreement with you and with myself. Chances are that you have never laid eyes on me in your life nor are you ever likely to if your luck holds out. I am going to treat you abysmally and you are going to suffer it. Agreed? I am going to waste your time by filling your mind with my own mental garbage and spurious self-abnegation.

Habitats you know nothing about. Of course I know that you think you do. You are wrong. Otherwise you would be writing this piece and I would be reading it and if you believe that you will believe anything.

In the summer of 1975 a group of North American people decided that it would be smart to put lots of other people, probably other North Americans, in very large cylinders filled with air and spinning to create a centrifugal force to replace gravity. Nice thought. Neat place to send murderers, lunatics, in-laws, people of absurd religious, political or racial disposition. You see the said cylinders lie almost a quarter of a million miles from both the Earth and the Moon following the latter around its one and a half million miles plus of orbit.

The trouble is their size. This varies from junior league model just six hundred feet across and with about one mile of fairly narrow 'countryside' sealed in on the inner rim of the wheel shape (or torus to the *cognoscenti*) to the Big Daddy which is nineteen miles long by four miles in diameter giving it an interior surface in the region of two hundred and thirty-nine square miles. Current thinking has it that there should be cute peek-a-boo windows running for miles down the cylinders to permit mirror reflected sunlight to enter. These mirrors should be imagined as being at least fifteen square miles apiece, the narcissist's delight.

Friends of mine fall about laughing in pubs when I describe habitats. Their fathers fell about laughing when my old man talked to them in pubs about moon shots. That's the trouble with this country, so much drink and crazy ideas the average person cannot stay upright for more than two minutes at a time.

So a habitat does seem like a crazy idea. I agree. Crossbows and steamships were crazy ideas too so we are off to a promising start. But how exactly do we start? How do we literally get the habitat off the ground? One thing is certain – forget about scientific research. When you are trying to convince someone about space applications and you feel an urge to mention ultra violet astronomical observatories or gravity waves excuse yourself from the company and gulp down a glass of vinegar. This should paralyse your speech making ability for the few minutes needed for the urge to pass. The very sensation should cleanse the brain as well as the throat.

Those who must be convinced are those who believe in money. Even the teeniest habitat will far outstretch the Apollo programme in terms of cash. Those who control disgustingly large sums of money must *want* to throw it to the skies before they will ever dream of doing so. What you talk about are investments and paying possibilities and financial incentives. You must learn a new way of thinking. That is what money really is when you analyse it. Money is a way of thinking and will be referred to hereafter as moneythink.

This is the cerebration process found in all commercial enterprises and the governments intimately connected with them. No government is going to build a habitat. Habitat building cannot be encompassed by moneythink. There are no references, no vocabulary nor syntax functions to make habitats meaningful in moneythink. Did someone say that habitats enhance the quality of life? Unfortunately that last phrase is also outside moneythink. The nearest function to it is the retail price index. But we do not despair.

Might not paranoia save us yet again?

Paranoia in the form of images like the frightening Commie-controlled Moon, the Western Imperialist drinking workers' blood cocktails on Mars, etc. provided the real launch vehicle for the Apollo lunar programme and the frantic Soviet attempts at placing soft landers on Venus and Mars. Certainly the paranoia was successful. It was modelled on the still continuing hassle over military superiority between Filthy Socialist Totalitarianism and Warmongering Capitalist Exploitation (both descriptions equally extreme and equally meaningless). No, it does look as if space-flight has just about exhausted its paranoia potential. If you point out the military advantages of a habitat (in-space manufacture of Sooper-dooper missiles, very cheap, thank you) and tell him the price of building the habitat just forget it. Some bright-eyed insanely misanthropic whiz kid is going to point out that for the same money he can supply a nice line in fifty megaton nuclear hand grenades for every front line infantryman (now that's what I call *hitting power*). No contest.

Paranoia is one channel to moneythink simply because fear operates at its basic emotional thought level as does greed. Knowing this we create our strategy.

Most people have heard of the energy crisis, the raw materials crisis, and the food crisis. In terms of moneythink these take the simplified form of rising prices. Optimists with blinding smiles talk of untapped resources for fossil fuels, fission reactors, the smelting of alternative ores (e.g. laterite instead of bauxite for aluminium), and T-bone soya steaks – textured of course. Well the waving fields of soya, sooper-dooper wheat, and cultivated submarine forests of edible seaweeds may take care of the chow problem and boost the tomato sauce industry. Maybe lower grade ores usage is at least a partial answer to the supply of metals problem, and an acceptable answer if the cost of smelting can be kept down.

But farming or smelting or simply watching a movie to forget about all problems you still need energy.

I don't like atomics.

It is a personal thing I have about radiation sickness. You know, one of those little fads.

Fortunately I am not alone in this. The prospect of several thousand large atomic power stations leaking quietly away all over the world does nothing for my insomnia problem. Nor does the vision of some cheery future newspaper article about the dramatic drop in the annual meltdown statistics. One meltdown is several million too many.

The solution to the fusion power station is going to pose more problems. No matter what answer is eventually found there will be the waste heat to be disposed of and the idea of pumping this into the sea in the form of warm water is troubling. I am unconvinced that hundreds or thousands of fusion stations pumping millions of tons of warmed water into the oceans will not interfere with ocean ecologies. As I write this there is speculation about the reason for the low numbers of salmon entering U.K. rivers. It is thought that the trouble is marine in origin and may be connected with the two degree temperature fluctuation recently observed in the North Sea near the Faeroes.

My friends the alternative technologists scream about these horrors of industrial intensive society too. They want control and conservation and a rational approach to the way humans live on earth and they are quite staggeringly naïve. Humans all understand and accept the concept of rationality but few are rational. Governments and financial powers are going to continue telling everyone that things really are quite rosy even when we all realize that we are in fact rushing headlong for the cliff edge. Governments who attempt to tell us the truth, that we must conserve, cut back, accept a lower standard of living etc., will be dealt with by being put out of office.

Some will combine their financial resources to go all-out for the fusion reactors which will lower energy costs and make expensive industrial processes relatively cheap once more. In a newly boosted industrial society like this the moneythinkers will probably go berserk tearing up as much ore from every conceivable part of the planet that they are allowed to. As the increasing number of fusion stations begins to interfere with the oceanic life systems, and consequently fewer and fewer are built, prices will begin to rise again. Energy production will no longer be keeping pace with energy requirements. The fusion stations will prove to be but a reprieve. So what do we do, resort to the windmills?

Not unlikely.

Tidal, wind, and geothermal power will probably be exploited to help pull down costs but alone they could not provide the quantity of energy which will be needed to support the growth oriented industries' requirements.

The answer lies in the much-slated concept of the geostationary solar power station, collecting its energy direct from the sun on vast arrays of cells and beaming this down to earth as low intensity microwave radiation. To build several thousand such stations at a cost competitive with that of the several thousand fusion stations ultimately required by a super-industrial society the capital outlay is initially very high. In business terms this is not a bad thing. In terms of money-think as opposed to those of non-profit space research thinking it is beautiful.

Put it this way. You have to spend ten units (each perhaps millions of dollars) over a period of ten years and all that time your units are slowly devaluing, say at a rate of five per cent per year. Naturally you want to go for an option which will use your money to the best advantage. One which allows you to buy more with what you have. Option 'A' allows you to spend eight units in the first year, one unit in the second year, and the last unit over the remaining eight years. This way you lose less than three per cent of your original buying power. Option 'B' allows you to spend one unit per year spread over the ten years. This way you lose almost twenty per cent of your investment's original buying power. And all this hot air puffed out about protecting your capital by incorporating the interest does not stand up either. That is purely for theoreticians. Moneythink is as illogical as any other average human thought process. In its terms large investment attracts more large investment. If someone who is believed shrewd throws a substantial hunk of his substantial fortune into an area completely ignored to date, then you can bet the fight to rapidly invest cash there will soon become a tooth and claw affair. Anyway, in ten years the value of the assets will more than compensate for a lack of investment interest if those assets are productive.

Do not hit me.

I am as much a professional economist as I am a space scientist.

But the basic argument stands.

Now the original investment is enough to send a shock of near fatal magnitude through any company secretary's nervous system. I am thinking of an investment in the region of between ten times and one hundred times that of the Apollo programme in the money value of the sixties. After that what you have to pay out is peanuts by comparison (okay – anything would be peanuts by comparison). Mainly what you have to keep up is a supply of hydrogen, carbon and oxygen flowing starwards in a steady stream. Everything else has been taken care of.

Interested, dear financial friend?

Let me tell you what you obtain for all that lovely money. Around 1990, that is if you start now, the first small-scale stations should be beaming back a trickle of wattage. This is still monstrously expensive per kilowatt-hour but is going to become startlingly cheaper. You also have funded the developing of a zero gravity factory pod based on Spacelab, the mini space station of the eighties. Naturally you waited until the North American and European philanthropic governments had developed Spacelab and the shuttle (a kind of muscled-up aircraft which can reach a fairly low earth orbit and return to fly again). Filthy Capitalist Exploitation of these facilities begins.

Let us call the combine of interests which is set in motion to make money from space the Skytank Corporation. Skytank owns three custom modified Spacelabs. To indicate the commercial value of these it employs one full time for the growth of large crystals thus eventually sending back a shuttle loaded with giant diamonds. There will be great protestations. The World Health Authority will shriek about the wastage of facilities which could have been producing much needed vaccines in a state of purity impossible to obtain on earth. Unless they are willing to pay a *lot* for the vaccines their protest-ations are as meaningless as ancient Etruscan script to the moneythinker. However the great rash of cardiac arrests in the diamond industry might just promote that well-heeled section of the community to take a very serious interest in space manufacture. There is no room in an article this size to give anything like a comprehensive list of zero gravity products. They range from 'perfect' ball bearings to exceptionally high-quality vacuum tubes for use in X-ray and laser technology. In fact they would promote a highly refined earth-based tech-nology operating at tolerances currently impossible to achieve.

So we have more interest. More business minds want into the Skytank operations. More money comes in. Space-oriented business becomes a growth industry reaching into the economies of all nations. Skytank wants to produce its own shuttles. Skytank wants bigger shuttles sooner. Skytank wants bigger factories. As soon as a permanent moon-base becomes feasible Skytank wants moon mining and smelting as it is going to be cheaper pulling the needed minerals down from the Moon than dragging them up from Earth. This is given a lot of backing by other financial concerns who are excited by the unique materials made possible by the Skytank factories. Variable-density alloys, the marriage of previously non-combinable substances, new strength-to-weight ratios, im-proved ductility, vastly improved temperature compatibility – all of these will have been available at very high cost and only utilized on a fairly restricted basis despite the increasing demand. Moon mining makes things so much easier all round. Man moves on to the lunar surface in force out of commercial expediency.

Skytank has large orbiting factories and stripmines on the moon. Since its early days it has been returning the cash inves-ted but has not yet broken even. All the countries concerned with it are still industry intensive. Their commitment to it is so enormous that they have to be. Their economies are coming to rely increasingly on a big return from space. A great deal of ground-based work must be done to support the programme in the manufacture of advanced shuttles and factory components and their related systems. The impact should keep unemployment figures on their hands and knees for a generation.

The dropping costs of returning goods from space puts the squeeze on other industries. Ground-based mining and metal industries feel the pressure. Those who wish to adapt throw their lot in with you know who. The rest adopt the same attitude that sailing ship owners once took to steam, and owners of passenger ship lines once took to the first transatlantic passenger flights. Their lack of vision will be understandable. They will continually think in terms of cargoes being lifted from the moon by space tug and lowered to earth by shuttle but for the most part bulk mineral transport will use neither of these.

A mass driver (or slingshot) will literally throw the partly-processed material off the moon to a collection point where it can then be shunted by tug to the Skytank factories. Cost savings here will be colossal. After being refined and worked upon, the goods will drop to earth upon an expendable wing called a waverider (it is so shaped that it rides its own hypersonic shockwave, surfboard style). The wings would be mass moulded in orbit from smelt waste and given as high a heat tolerance as possible. There would be a small re-usable guidance package aboard to help it down. Waveriders have very large 'footprints' or possible landing areas when descending from orbit, so, with the use of a few solid fuel rockets and parachute arrays they could drop their loads fairly accurately and cheaply in most of the required areas.

Did someone just shout 'Rubbish'?

Let me say unto the doubter that what may appear to be beyond the wondrous powers of technology is as naught before the miraculous powers of mammon!

The relatively expensive business of space factory construction is now taking place almost wholly from parts manufactured in space. The ground based industries dependant on factory part/system manufacture are now being phased over to the unique materials exploitation. Let us take electronics as an example. Timebase International Electrics invested heavily in Skytank at the start on condition that it could tender for factory module electronics. Several generations of these systems have succeeded each other and Timebase currently hires factory space from Skytank (as a preferred customer this comes at a reduced rate). Here it uses the technology evolved in space for the production of cheap but exceptionally high quality components. The Timebase ground factories which were once involved in component manufacture are now involved in assembly. Around this time ground assembly is concentrating on non-space usage. Soon all but a few in-space articles will be manufactured in space and the value of what comes down far exceeds what is coming up from ground.

We are now in the mid to late 'nineties and Skytank has more than recouped its original investment. The products of space factories play a major part in world economics and that part becomes greater year by year. No one has the slightest doubt about the viability of in-space manufacture by this time. It is only natural that the energy crisis may be viewed differently when it is possible to construct enormous solar power stations relatively inexpensively.

So far Skytank has been bread and butter oriented. Now it is time for the thick strawberry jam.

Over the next decade the construction of test stations from lunar materials will take place. Then the big contract arrives, a contract for, say, a score of geosynchronous stations. The number will be around this size to offset the costs absorbed in setting up an acceptable permanent home for the thousands of people who will be involved in the power station construction over the ten year period. Many of these individuals will have their first experience of zero gravity construction work in the building of the habitat. By the time they have completed the first twenty stations they will be able to drop their rates for the next twenty as they already have their habitat constructed and functional.

Given the option of living aboard a station/factory habitat rather than the less agreeable quarters aboard an orbital factory more and more individuals are going to plump for the rolling meadows of the habitat.

Given the option of living aboard a station/factory habitat rather than the less agreeable quarters aboard an increasingly overcrowded planet with its international tensions, its housing problems, its wars, its increasingly restricted opportunities, its eternal difference between those who have and those who have not, its reduction of people to ciphers, its nuclear terrorism, more and more individuals are going to plump for the rolling meadows of the habitat.

Sooperjuicey protein plus vitamin-burstin' chewtextured soybeef steakburgers versus pork and free range chicken.

Again, no contest!

The industry-intensive society has been lifted bootstrap fashion into space. The first quarter of the next century will not see ground-based industry eclipsed by the space factory but no one will have the slightest doubt that the trend lies in this direction. So, to recap, what you have for your money is the most highly sophisticated industry man has ever known and a secure future for the technology based culture now extending itself into the twenty-first century. In detail what you have is a selection of factories which outmatch anything on earth in their performance. They produce more, better, faster, simply because they have no pollution worries and a virtually endless energy supply from the sun. The techniques of providing these factories with power have been refined high enough to provide old mother Earth herself with energy at bargain basement cost. You have a habitat wherein the quality of life is equal to and in many cases surpasses the quality of ground life.

Plans are afoot for 'Utopian' habitats, 'pleasure dome' habitats, 'people's' habitats, 'military' habitats and dozens of other types. Their main business is constructing factory facilities and still more power stations to supply these facilities with energy. They also build more habitats.

So far so good.

We are now at the end of the first quarter of the next century. In terms of your original investment you are not merely clear; you are rolling in the crinkly green stuff. You are ahead, way ahead.

What happens to Skytank then becomes more a matter of politics than economics. With such a powerful industrial economic complex beyond the home world this is only natural. The situation is not that of colonies who almost out of historical obligation yearn for independence. The struggle will emerge between Skytank and the earth-bound parent companies who formed it. Who controls whom? As a large slice of the national budgets of most major industrial nations will be entwined in this argument we have a situation of the earther versus the habitee.

Around this time Skytank executives will look to the asteroid belt and the outer planet moons for supplies of those elements, nitrogen, hydrogen and carbon, which they have previously obtained from ground sources. There will be enormous pressure mounted by Earthside interests to curtail any projects which might bring closer total Skytank economic independence of the home world.

The fight for self-control and self-decision-making abilities could last for decades but I do not want to trail this projection too far ahead. Let us say that by the middle of the twenty-first century we have an independent Skytank for all intents and purposes. The habitees are now almost without any reliance on ground. The ground now finds prices rising yet again.

Ground now competes for habitat commerce with other habitats. Although Earth is still the main, and in some cases only, source for certain rare materials and certain technologies crucial to the developing in-space habitee culture there is no question of earth withholding these. The balance of functional dependence now lies squarely in favour of Skytank.

Whether Skytank could continue to exist for any length of time under these conditions is a moot point. As the numbers of habitats and habitees rise, maintaining the integral structure of the Corporation will become increasingly difficult. Some groups of power-seeking habitees will probably form small independent companies which will initially lease manpower and equipment from Skytank until they can build their own. These little companies will almost certainly be highly specialist in nature, supplying Skytank with services and then in turn serving one another as they grow both in number and strength.

The political importance of the terrestrial powers is already secondary in their eyes. Many of them may regard ground society as a massive but decrepit beast, slowly being crushed to death by its own weight. Ground will always be supplied with trading goods and electricity if only to keep the formidable array of Earthside weaponry at bay.

The day when the bulk of human population will be spread more evenly between ground and space is already just coming into the offing. One of ground's big value products is a mass of highly trained subject specialists which the habitat companies are more than anxious to snap up. Business is booming at such a rate they need every top man and woman that they can lay their hands on.

Now let us look back at what the original investment was and what it was intended to cover. In terms of finance it was microscopic, dollar value to dollar value, compared with the new-found wealth in that gold mine in the sky. Ultimately it was intended to provide fairly cheap electricity on an increasing scale to support growth industry. By the middle of the next century we have myriads of stations supplying all the power needed for Earth and space industry. The stations are not just in orbit about the Earth any longer. Hundreds of immense structures are flying majestically in a much closer orbit about the Sun than Mercury and beaming back energy via high intensity laser to 'busbar' relays which stream this to dozens of other receptors. And no longer just those in the Earth-Moon system. Planet Four, a group interested in the commercial possibilities of Mars have started constructing the first habitat to circle that world. They are utilizing material shipped out from the Moon but are principally concerned with mining Phobos the inner martian satellite for the bulk of minerals. Other plans are afoot. Designs for highly mobile habitats are being tested, habitats which would sail throughout the solar system and not just about the earth.

I write science fiction. You might suspect that I have taken numerous liberties with possibility because of this. You would be absolutely accurate. But before you call me an ignorant, irresponsible, cretin remember two things. Firstly, I am six feet tall, weigh over fourteen stone and learned how to deal with insults on the streets of Glasgow's east end. Secondly, I know that this whole projection is riddled through with elements which will prove different in nature when, and if, they do occur, but I refuse to be guilty of a failure of nerve. Arthur Clarke, rightly in my opinion, points to this as the inexcusable failure in his essays on 'The Hazards of Prophecy'.

Boyce's neck is sticking out by a mile. Let me stretch it a shade further for your entertainment.

Already materials scientists are talking about the possibilities of clever matter, matter which changes its character and properties according to a prearranged programme. Considering the boost to material science which will come from space factories, I predict that one of the big lurches forward by humankind before the end of the century will be a wide range of clever materials, complete with software, commercially available from Skytank or whatever the space interests group calls itself.

Clever materials will also be used extensively in orbital constructions including the habitats themselves.

What of the habitees?

As was pointed out earlier the good Earth may not appear quite so good when measured up against the habitat. The more refined the habitat technology, the longer the habitats have existed, the more acceptable and attractive life in space becomes. Ask the average bloke in a pub what he thinks of living in an O'Neill habitat, after describing one, and he'll look at you as if you have newly stepped out of a sewer.

But frontiers are compulsive places.

They will come at first in tens and hundreds. They will be scientists, technologists and medical experts to begin with, but even they will not be quite the same as their wholly earth-bound colleagues. Like the less research-oriented men and women who follow there will be a trace of the hard romantic in them. Blazing trails has always attracted those who are tough, practical and imaginative. When the initial habitat settlements are taking on a permanent identity these should form an enviable gene pool.

What about advances in biological engineering? What about the sooperdooper computers and the artificial intelligences? What about contact of some form with another civilization across interstellar space? I do not think that any of these will drastically alter the fundamental picture. Certainly, the extent to which they impinge on the habitat culture will closely affect the detail of everyday life, but the economic base upon which they function will be much as described above.

Life in a habitat might well prove unsettling to a groundee sixty or seventy years from now. By then the ground culture could well be that of the highly mobile individual and the 'plug-in' lifestyle. The habitat lifestyle, on the other hand, would be dominated by the high degree of social interaction between co-habitees. Bob Shaw's 'Small World' highlights this aspect perfectly. It may prove to be the main psychological barrier between what will by then be two human types: the spacer who has a strong sense of community, group identity, home – call it what you will – and the groundee growing more nomadic, self-obsessed, and isolated.

That is just about it. I have a splitting headache and am desperate to abandon this typewriter (which I simply *must* clean tomorrow). But before I go let me remind you that 2050 is less than seventy-five years hence. That means there are kids about today, who should live to see all this come true or crack-up with laughter at how inaccurate it is. Or both?

And perhaps it is not fair to go back about seventy-five years to gain a perhaps faulty perspective in relation to our own world. In 1902 the first man crossed the Irish Channel in a balloon, the arc generator was invented, and Nernst's postulated 'third law of thermodynamics' was the talk of the scientific establishment.

A parting vision.

Chris Boyce

We are in a superhabitat and it is a special occasion. Window picnics are always special occasions. This one takes place at night and thousands of kids are trekking out across Window Cee with packed snacks and covered flasks in their hands. Just before midnight all chat and laughter ceases. They sit down, squat, or lie full out face down. From somewhere a light breeze introduces the fragile aroma of mimosa. On cue the great mirror peels glittering back. Before and below them they see Saturn, its vast rings spread out like curving planes away and behind. They are dropping to where they will hurtle round the dark side and slingshot back into the solar system. And the pale tints of the giant planet are growing more monstrous, more magnificent.

In a sky
the colour
of Coca-Cola . . .

In Search of
Professor Greatrex

Michael Coney

The prison was no better or worse than the others I'd seen; just the usual chunky admission of man's failure to come to terms with himself. The Governor sat behind the usual littered desk, his back to the dust-stained window. The air smelled of stewed cabbage and old sneakers. From the depths of the building came a rhythmic hammering as the inmates expressed their collective disapproval of something. I heard a guard shouting.

The Governor had been haranguing a prison officer over the visiphone; now he switched off, turned to me and said, 'Yes?' He looked surprised to see a woman within this unhappy male preserve.

I showed him my card. I explained that I was writing a thesis for my Sociology Doctorate on the subject of Group Relationships in the late Twentieth, and that I kept coming up against a brick wall. 'I find references to a Professor M. C. Greatrex and some paper he wrote which represented a turning point in inter-racial and international relationships. It seems the paper came out around 1978, and from what I can find out about the Professor he would have been thirty-three at the time. Which would make him seventy-one now, if he's still alive.'

The Governor said flatly, 'He was transferred.'

'Oh. That's what I was told at the last prison, and the one before. Listen . . .' I was getting desperate. 'Somewhere there must be a permanent record of his whereabouts. A prisoner can't get lost within the system, surely? Why all these transfers?'

'For his own good, I guess.'

'Protection, you mean? I can't find a record of his trial, or even his crime!'

'Yeah, well, don't go getting all hysterical about it, huh? If a guy's in jail, you can bet he's in for a good reason.' He was riffling through a card index. He pressed a button and a visual display lit up.

'Well?'

'He was transferred to Willsworthy Heights, Ms Kwai. Twelve years ago.'

It was like a treasure hunt. I hoped the prize would be worth the effort.

It was at Brendon that I had my first real break. The pattern emerging indicated that the Professor was transferred 'for his own good' about once a year and was still alive seven years ago.

The Brendon Governor had something more for me, however – a small box of possessions.

'It came with him, and somehow he left without it.'

I asked why it hadn't been forwarded, and the answer was typical of bureaucratic thinking. The box hadn't come to light for a few years, by which time the Professor had already been moved on several times. Since it was too much trouble to track him down, the box had been shelved.

'You can pass it on to him, or his heirs,' said the Governor. 'There's nothing in it. Just a few dollars and some papers. The usual sort of thing. A bunch of keys. Sign here, please.'

Clutching the box, I left. He was glad to see the back of us both.

The papers were yellowed and stained with some nameless prison exudation. They were valuable to me, almost beyond belief. In time I came to know their contents by heart.

Among the papers was part of *the Paper*. A few pages from the original manuscript. There was also a loose clip of letters from Professor Greatrex's colleagues. And a small notebook in the form of a diary, covering the period 1975 to 1986. This latter was of great interest in that it explained many of the events which took place after the initial publication of the Paper – but it was the Paper itself which held the key to the whole affair.

Quote from Dr Branislawski, letter dated 20 June 1978: 'What I can't understand, Professor – and neither I nor any of the Society will readily forgive you for this – is why you should have first aired your paper *On Man and his Intellect* in a *science fiction publication*! Are you thereby attempting to discount the truth of your theories, to partially disown them, in some childish way to imply: honest, I didn't mean it?'

Extract from the Paper, *On Life and Intellect* [*sic!*] by Professor M. C. Greatrex:

'*Intelligence*. In laymens' terms, "intelligence" is generally understood to mean the capacity to learn. It is difficult to imagine a more clumsy definition, since virtually all living things have the capacity to learn in one way or another, otherwise they would not have survived. Whereas the layman habitually implies that man (and perhaps the great apes and *delphinidae*) are the only creatures on Earth possessing "intelligence", in fact the lowest plant – treated as a species – might be said to have the capacity for learning, by the very fact that it evolves to suit its environment.

'A narrower and consequently more satisfactory definition is used in psychology, thus: "Intelligence is the capacity to acquire knowledge or understanding and to use it in novel situations." Even this asks more questions than it answers, however – the most immediate being (a) how do we measure capacity? and (b) how do we define the degree of novelty of the situation? But we have, at least, disposed of the chrysanthemum as a potential rival to man's intellect.

'In order to separate man from his fellow-travellers on Earth we devised the intelligence test – and what a cumbersome device it was! In quite arbitrary fashion an English intelligence test would eliminate a child whose only language was Swahili, since that child could not understand the instructions. This problem was quickly eradicated, but quickly gave birth to another: a child from the African bush simply does not deal in the same concepts as a child from Pittsburgh.

It rapidly became evident that any meaningful intelligence test must take into account the environment in which the child was raised. (You will notice I speak only of children; the significance of this will become evident later.) And as for the dolphins – well, we were unable to learn their language or adapt our tests to their environment. So we concluded they were stupid ... I am not being facetious – by our definitions they *were* stupid.

'You can see what is happening. We are retreating even further from a neat, positive and convincing definition of "intelligence". We are hedging. Let us return to our psychological definition and start again.

'Let us, in fact, split "intelligence" into two distinct functions. Let us define them as (a) the capacity to learn and (b) the capacity to apply this learning to novel situations. And let us further state that the novel situation will be realistic in terms of the environment – and that a measure of intelligence is the degree of novelty with which the individual can cope.

'And let us free ourselves of that final pitfall: the concept that all men are equal. While agreeing that they should be allowed equal rights (whatever form those rights may take) let us be honest, and freely admit that a very bright Tasaday tribesman may prove very dumb when transported to Paris, and that this is in the nature of things. And let us not deny that evolution has shaped different races to suit their differing environments, and that a new-born aboriginal child, reared in Vancouver, would never perform miracles of differential calculus; neither would an Edinburgh baby be physically equipped for hunting tapir in the Amazon basin. Thousands of years of evolution have shaped our minds and bodies in different ways.'

'He was transferred,' said the Governor of Broadstreet Penitentiary. 'He was only here for a month.'

'Why?'

'Trouble. The usual thing. It seemed one of the older prisoners had been involved with him years ago, in some way. He told a few of the thugs about him. I don't know what he said, but it was enough to get old Greatrex smashed up. He was in intensive care for three weeks, then we moved him on to Lowgate. There's no alternative, in cases like this.'

Outside it was spring, and a climbing plant was clothing the forbidding walls with new leaves. I wondered: will prisons ever change? Will the time ever come when a person can be cured of antisocial tendencies? Not by anything so crude as lobotomy; just some injection which will neutralize whatever is wrong with his body chemistry . . .

Or is the urge to kill, steal and cheat a vital factor in our make-up; part of that which makes us human, another manifestation of our will to love, discover and multipy?

Quote from Professor Ferber, letter dated 3 September 1978. 'The truth or otherwise of your theories is of no interest to myself or to the Department. Your crime lies in publishing them.'

Extract from the Paper, *On Life and Intellect.*

'. . . but the technique for answering I.Q. tests can be learned – and in fact there are many private tutors who specialize in teaching these techniques to children and job applicants. This obviously invalidates the I.Q. test as a reliable method of measuring intellectual capacity.

'It is perhaps more profitable to turn our attention to the second factor in the composition of that thing which we call intelligence: the capacity to apply learned data to novel situations. How novel? Well, perhaps a measure of the novelty is a true measure of intelligence – and here we begin to move into the fascinating realm of creative reasoning and its human manifestation in the ultimate – genius.

'And now the value of our two subdivisions becomes apparent. Learning, considered simply as the accumulation of knowledge, continues throughout the lifetime of the individual. But the growth of creative reasoning power – quite a different thing – ceases abruptly with the change in hormone production at puberty.

'At puberty, a person is at the peak of his creative reasoning ability and, regrettably, begins to go steadily downhill from that time on.

'The reason for this lies in the evolution of man. And here is the first novel proposition which I would like to put to you. Man did *not* evolve in the manner normally surmised; that is, as a result of a favourable mutation – increased brain capacity with an attendant rise in intelligence – bringing him down from the trees and putting a club in his hand, the use of which required further exercise of his new brain powers. This simply *does not fit*. It does not account for primitive man's enormous *theoretical* capacity for creative reasoning (based on cranial capacity) which was far ahead of the requirements of the Lower Pleistocene.

'Instead, I propose that man was the result of an *unfavourable mutation*. The first man was not a halfways-intelligent ape. Rather, he was an ape with an extraordinarily long and vulnerable childhood. *He simply did not grow up when he should have* – there have been plenty of similar recorded instances among other animals, but without this momentous result.

'He was puny and unless he was protected for a perilously long time, he died. Many of these strange ape-children died.

'But a few survived. With a soft skull and twice the time of an ape to develop, they survived to a new, later maturity. And the inevitable result of this long period of brain growth was superior creative reasoning capacity. This was passed on down the generations – and man was on his feet.'

'What kind of a man was he?' I asked.

'Uh, quiet. Nothing exceptional. He kept pretty much away from the other prisoners. For good reason, I guess.'

'But what about the fits of violence? The times he attacked the guards – and those other times, when he had to be restrained from injuring himself?'

'I don't know where you heard that.'

'Well, I'd read ... What little I could find out from old newspapers and such, he seemed to be some kind of a madman.'

The Governor raised his eyebrows. 'I'd have said he was a

model prisoner, Ms Kwai. I even recommended him for parole, but it was turned down flat.'

'Why?'

'They wouldn't say.'

Quote from *Cape Town Herald*, 28 December 1979. 'Christmas Day witnessed the symbolic cremation of the last relics of apartheid. Whites and Blacks alike danced and sang around a huge bonfire in Kennedy Square as two buses, a mound of "Whites Only" signs, and an effigy of Professor M. C. Greatrex went up in smoke. Elsewhere, architects and engineers moved into Black areas in the first phase of Operation Brotherhood . . . As a matter of editorial policy, it has been decided to discontinue the use of the racist terms "White" and "Black" when referring to human beings.'

Letter from J. Singleton, 15 March 1980. 'Understand you received a life sentence for – treason, did they call it? Well, I hope this reaches you. Here in Winnipeg we're just feeling the effects of Operation Brotherhood; some fifteen thousand people from Nigeria arrived and moved straight into the recently-vacated houses. It's working out better than I could have believed. I see no signs of resentment over the forced move; in fact, our own people caused far more difficulty when they were shipped out earlier. The Nigerians have fitted straight into their jobs and are mixing well socially – which after all, is the whole point of the thing. I see Winnipeg as being a totally integrated city – whatever that means – by the end of the year.'

Letter from Dr Klaus, 22 October 1980. 'Incidentally, has it ever occurred to that twisted mind of yours that you were, in a perverse way, *responsible* for Operation Brotherhood?'

Extract from the diary of Professor Greatrex, *circa* December 1980. 'Who would have believed that the first signs of *real* guilt, of a real desire to make amends far different from the previous hypocrisy and tokenism, consumed the Caucasian race when faced with a situation *for which they were not to*

blame. Nobody was to blame – except perhaps myself, as my ex-friend Ferber would have me believe. But is it a crime to tell the people the truth? Particularly when nothing but good has come out of it? I sincerely believe I committed no crime. I merely offered myself up as a scapegoat. Jesus Christ did the same ... Must be careful of dangerous trains of thought ...'
(Here the writing deteriorated, as though the Professor was undergoing severe inward turmoil as he wrote.)

Extract from the Paper, *On Life and Intellect*.

'It is reasonable to assume that human childhood is *no longer than it need be*. Throughout the ages the developing human animal has been weeded out by its very vulnerability, so that the pre-pubescent period has reached a minimum timespan compatible with adequate creative reasoning capacity. The necessary length of childhood varies according to the accustomed environment of the generations over which the weeding-out process occurred. The adult continues to *learn*, but will have *no more creative reasoning* capacity than is necessary for him to deal with those novel situations which he will encounter in his accustomed environment.

'Environments differ. Some – the Arctic regions – are so inhospitable that man did not reach them until comparatively late in his development, by which time he was equipped to deal with them. Others – the temperate zones – offer a challenge. They are mild enough for man to survive his long childhood yet changeable enough to stimulate him into maximum realization of his potential. And others again – the tropical regions – are places of quick growth, violent life and death, with the emphasis on early maturity in order that man may be able to defend himself the more quickly.

'Statistics bear out the hypothesis. On average, a child whose racial background lies in the tropics will reach adolescence 1.9 years earlier than his counterpart in the temperate zones.

'And so to the second novel proposition ... Such tropical children, through no fault of their own, will average some 20% less creative reasoning capacity than their temperate cousins.

'Simply because of the different environment in which they have evolved, resulting in a shorter childhood, they will be less intelligent. True, they will be superior physically – but what use is that to them, in an increasingly mechanized and technological world?

'I am aware of the despair, the horror – and the accusations – which my findings will cause. I can do nothing about it. The answer, if there is an answer, lies in a full-scale programme of integration – and I mean *compulsory integration* – world-wide.

'Only by interbreeding can man – who places such great store in equality – live with his conscience.'

In such a way Professor Greatrex presaged Operation Brotherhood.

And at last, in Georgetown, I met Mrs Greatrex. She told me she visited her husband once a week. She'd moved from town to town, following his trail – which ought to have told me something about her, I guess.

'I have an appointment with the Governor tomorrow,' I told her. 'I'm hoping to see the Professor in the afternoon.' Although my quest was almost over, my motives for meeting Professor Greatrex had become distinctly ambiguous.

'Give him my love, Ms Kwai,' she said simply.

It was a small apartment; a bookcase caught my eye. Books by Aldiss, Clarke, Silverberg, people I'd never heard of. And a row of books by Greatrex, labelled science fiction. Science fiction! I might have guessed. 'Do you have a published copy of his paper, *On Life and Intellect?*' I asked. 'I only have a few pages of the original manuscript. There's quite a lot missing.'

'You have the original?' She was staring at me. 'I wonder … Maybe you'd let me have it. I . . . I have little enough of his.'

She spoke as though this odious Paper – I was beginning to detest both the fabric and content of the leprous pages – was something precious.

127

'I'd be happy to exchange it for the published version.'

She looked helpless. 'I don't have one. Nobody has one that I know of. Didn't you know? The publication it appeared in was withdrawn immediately and I think most of the sold copies were tracked down. There was a lot of trouble.' Her voice, her expression were almost proud now; she was reliving her wretched little husband's one hour of glory. 'Afterwards, Xeroxed copies appeared for a while ...' She frowned. 'I guess the wrong sort of people got hold of them and started using the article as a ... political tool. Then everybody seemed suddenly to get, well ... *ashamed*, and it all went quiet, and the next thing was this Brotherhood thing.'

Yes ... I suppose humanity would unite, when faced with the ultimate evil. Not before.

The woman's attitude was annoying me. It was apparent that – after all these years and against all the evidence – she still regarded Greatrex as some kind of hero. 'Listen to me,' I said. 'I don't think you quite understand. Maybe it's a long time since you read your husband's Paper.' I took the sheets from my briefcase. 'I'll read some of it to you ...'

Extract from the Paper, *On Life and Intellect.*

'... so, although in the Lower Pleistocene a woman might have been engaged in repetitive household tasks whereas a man was selected by the more demanding adaptive aspects of the hunt – in the present day (evolution having been buffered by civilization) it seems there is little to prevent the two sexes learning similar jobs and being able to perform them equally well.

'Apart from one little thing – that sudden halt in growth of creative reasoning capacity. Because *boys reach puberty almost two years after girls.* Millennia ago this was necessary due to the more demanding nature of the male role. Girls show a compensatory temporary increase in *learning speed* shortly before puberty, but no corresponding acceleration in reasoning capacity. For this reason we have (just one example among many) the demonstrated reluctance of women to become involved in the complex logic of mathematical fields even when it provides a sure route to the higher executive positions in business. The very fact that our society is financially oriented is the reason why so few women find positions of power. And we have only to examine the comparative performances of the sexes in the world of art to find many instances of this creative differential.

'Unfortunate it may be; but in terms of the actual period of time during which creative reasoning capacity develops, the puberty lag means that men have, on average, some 22% more creative reasoning capacity than women.

'Homosexuals score very highly here; statistically they develop later than straights – more evidence that they are born, not made. Only prejudice keeps them from the top in fields which require the support of their fellow men. Individualistically, in the arts for example, their superior creative ability is demonstrable. Those few people we class as geniuses have also been shown to be late sexual developers, where such personal information is available . . .'

I said to her, 'Can't you see what kind of a man your husband is?'

She said, 'I always knew.'

Why should I bother? Why in hell should I concern myself – simply because I fail a test devised to different standards than the ones I operate on? If a man says to me: 'The most important thing in the world is intelligence *as defined by me*,' why in hell should I believe him? If his kind of intelligence puts him in *what he considers to be* a position of power, why should I bother to challenge him? Why not set my own female standards, equally as valid as his by *my* reckoning, and excel by those standards?

Why do I tremble with frustration? I will *not* cry.

So the cell door swung open and the keys jingled, swinging. The room was bare; just a basin and a toilet, a table and a chair on which sat an old man. His hair was wispy, his cheeks hollow as though his gums had not held teeth for a very long time. He stood, and his pants were baggy, his sex oddly neuter.

I'd expected something different. I'd visualized Professor Greatrex as a *man*, with all that infuriatingly implies. Not a slack-lipped, slack-loined wreck.

Something grew in me, a sort of triumph.

Before me was the cause of it all, the evil being which had wrecked the lives of all women of all races; the scapegoat – and he was indeed that; a beaten old goat.

I'd intended to read his Paper to him, to question him on some of his reasoning; but cogent argument would be wasted on this dotard.

I made to slip the Paper back in my briefcase – but he caught sight of it. He recognized it. The light returned to his eyes, suddenly they were wild, and he was backing away. He uttered a croak.

He cried, 'I didn't write it! For God's sake, it wasn't me! It was somebody else – one of my students. One of my students. I stole his idea.'

'The handwriting, the corrections – they're all yours. You're lying.' I never wanted to leave that cell. I wanted to punish him for all of time. I wanted to stand here forever, accusing him with my sex, contradicting him with my power. I felt a sudden urge to take my clothes off, to display myself in front of him, to challenge him to sexual combat.

His pose was unconsciously dramatic, back pressed against the wall, head averted as if to duck a blow, eyes slyly askance, peering at the Paper. 'It wasn't me,' he whispered. 'Not me . . . Somebody else.'

And suddenly I was through, disgusted. The enemy, the archetype of evil, was simply a cowardly old man. I swallowed, wanting to vomit. The cell stank. I turned away. I walked out, past the guard, through the door.

Mrs Greatrex was standing there.

She said casually, as if it didn't matter, 'I have a couple of things for you. This –' She handed me a small wrapped package, book-sized. Her eyes were turned away; she looked past me into the cell, '– and this.' Now her gaze met mine.

She struck me across the face with astonishing force.

Off balance, I fell against the wall, smashing my temple

against the brick. I felt the guard's hand on my arm, steadying me. I shook it off.

I'm changing the subject of my Doctorate thesis for ethical reasons; I can't bring myself to research further into a subject which is so clouded with lies and prejudice that the truth, or the importance of truth, is forgotten. I sometimes wonder if the Paper *was* responsible for Operation Brotherhood. It is difficult to imagine the whole world being moved to panic because of its own guilt complex and the bigotry of one man.

And Operation Brotherhood cannot help women . . .

Mrs Greatrex once said to me, 'He never had a proper trial, then they jailed him for treason. Treason! Who was he supposed to have betrayed?'

And I replied, 'The human race.'

It was a neat and satisfactory reply, if of doubtful logic. It made me feel better. She'd said nothing, merely gazing at me stupidly, like an old sheep. An old sheep married to an old goat.

I can laugh about it now. I still have the ridiculous paperback on my bookshelf and once in a while I take it down and again read Professor Greatrex's preposterous claims. Of course, I have the full text now. Some of the additional matter is even more laughable and the final paragraphs reveal all too clearly the Professor's background in science fiction.

Extract from the Paper, *On Life and Intellect*.

'All this has happened, all this is in the past. If we still maintain that intelligence – and its inevitable ticket to positions of power – is the yardstick by which we judge our fellow men, then there is little more that can be done except interbreeding, as I have stated before.

'So what of the future of man? I regret that my final proposition holds out no hope for the descendants of you or me.

'For children are maturing earlier, just a little bit, every generation. All children, of whatever sex or race. The statistical evidence cannot be refuted. Each new child has a fraction less time to develop creative reasoning capacity than its parents had. Each generation is a little less smart.

'I see man drifting down a slow tide of devolution, having for a short time enjoyed the gift of a chance mutation – long childhood – and now returning inexorably and irreversibly to the norm for his species, a pre-pubescent period of – what?

'Five years, like a gibbon?'

Like many of his ilk, Professor Greatrex was fond of the disaster story.

Once More, With Feeling

Stan Gooch

The universe and human society in many ways function as a gigantic Rorschach or Thematic Apperception Test, in which man discovers only the shape of his own consciousness ... The revealed Mr Hyde is no less evolved than Dr Jekyll. But like his counterparts the werewolf and the vampire, Hyde is fully active only at night, and his passing then remembered only in imagination.

The Jews represent less than one per cent of the world's population. Yet since the inception of the Nobel Prizes at the beginning of this century, sixteen per cent of the individual Prize winners have been Jewish. In more recent years the percentage has risen. During 1960–69 the figure rose to twenty-five per cent, and shows every sign of increasing further – the more remarkable in that there are considerably fewer Jews in the world now than there were in 1939.

Yet Jewish boys, my dear Professor Greatrex, reach puberty about a year earlier than WASPs.

A. C. Kinsey noted in his famous *Sexual Behaviour in the Human Male* that boys who reach puberty early are twice as likely to practise homosexuality as those who reach it at average age. Yet there is no evidence that Jewish boys – or African boys – are more homosexual than any WASP group. Rather the contrary, I would say.

So with all respect to Greatrex – and I *do* respect him – matters are not really that simple.

But yet again, they are not imponderable. As a schoolboy, for example, I puzzled for several years over why the French said '*quinze jours*' (fifteen days) when they meant a fortnight. Then I understood – just try saying '*quatorze jours*'. So there *is* a reason for everything; and if we keep looking hard enough, we find that reason.

133

My own conviction is that the only way in which any organism can be studied, or understood, is by the simultaneous consideration of every aspe ct of its being–itsbiology, physiology, psychology, chemistry, ontogeny, phylogeny, and so forth. My own private dream is that some day there will be only one study of man, called life science. The course leading to qualification would last, say, ten years, or perhaps twenty. It would require proficiency in every subject whatsoever having any bearing whatsoever on any aspect whatsoever of man.

It is, however, absolutely typical of the psychologists of Professor Greatrex's generation that they sought to understand man's behaviour by reference to single, or to one or two variables only, progressing sometimes even as far (good heavens!) as three factor analysis.

Intelligence tests themselves are at first sight a good idea, at second a bad idea, at third not quite such a bad idea – within, nevertheless, their inherent limitations.

The hope of intelligence testers is to somehow measure in a reliable way the differences in ability which obviously exist between organisms of the same species, principally between human beings. More ambitious projects follow from this. Perhaps, for instance, we can distinguish between innate ability and ability actually developed in response to varying environmental conditions. Perhaps tests on the young will enable us to predict later ability in the adult. Along with the hope of measuring the *potential* of individuals comes the hope of measuring the potential of entire species – so that this, among other things, can then be compared with the species-intelligence of other types of organism.

However, the test designed to compare the abilities of elephants and crocodiles is a flop. The crocodile scores zero on squirting water through his nose, while the elephant does badly swimming a measured course underwater.

Oh, yes – but surely these things are not intelligence? Well, perhaps not. But then one has to say where 'those things' leave off and intelligence begins. For, in any case, you can only ever test what animals (and people) *actually do*. And the central problem is not just one of creating a 'culture free' test (that is, one which bypasses any conscious or unconscious training an individual has received) but a 'physiology free' one. In respect of this last remark, and in summary, I have to say that anyone is a fool or a sociologist if he thinks that psychology is not a branch of physiology (and physiology a branch of psychology). Professor Greatrex himself certainly was aware of that. But still, what *about* culture?

As already suggested, and as quickly realized by the researchers involved, tests designed for Europeans proved very unfair and unreliable when used on Africans, Aborigines, Chinese or Red Indians. Even the so-called abstract shapes and patterns of the non-verbal tests were found to be culture-bound and experience-bound. One example illustrates the amazing extent of the blocks and pitfalls involved. When the first European ships reached the shores of the unexplored southern continents, the natives were unable to perceive the vessels the sailors came in as boats. These were so much larger than anything the natives themselves built that they were completely unable to accommodate them – not just conceptually, but visually.

Many psychologists seem today to have abandoned the hope of ever using intelligence tests to compare the ability and intelligence levels of different ethnic and cultural groups. But I think they have given up prematurely. If you wish to have intelligence testing (and I personally do not), there are still ways of proceeding.

For example, when a 'European' intelligence test is given to a group of Australian Aborigines, although all do absolutely badly as compared with any European sample, nevertheless some Aborigines do better than some other Aborigines. The test *does* therefore still reveal a relative ability or 'pecking' order within the tribe. So despite its absolute weaknesses and unfairness, this test is, nevertheless, measuring intelligence. In fact I think we have the very measure which Greatrex requires.

Greatrex: *Intelligence is the capacity . . . to use
understanding in novel situations.*

The European intelligence test – for the Aborigine – is from
every standpoint a novel situation.

There is no need to stop here. Let us apply our insight further. Let us, by the usual methods, construct a fair intelligence
test for the Bongo Bongo people of northern Gish and standardize it on that population. Then let us also construct and
standardize a fair test for the Fagawi nation of eastern Pish.
Now let us give the Bongo test to the Fagawi, and the Fagawi
test to the Bongos. Does not a comparison of the difference in
scores achieved on the two tests in each country give us a fair
measure of the 'novelty quotient' of each tribe?

I think we have thus answered Greatrex's central question
and moreover in purely operational terms.

Greatrex: *How do we define the degree of novelty
of a situation?*

However, the cultural aspects are really the least of the problem, as Greatrex had himself begun to see. The question cannot be examined from such a superficial standpoint. For, once
again, anyone is a fool or a sociologist or a philosopher if he
thinks that culture is not a branch of physiology (and physiology a branch of culture).

Though Greatrex had clearly begun to appreciate the truth
of this last remark, the variable he chose to focus upon was, I
think, one of the least important – taken in isolation, that is.
In other words, like so many psychologists of his day, he
hopelessly oversimplified the position, and the task facing
him. We have already seen, for instance, that Jewish boys, who
reach puberty a year earlier than Caucasians, nevertheless far
exceed them in all forms of ability. The Nobel Prizes, after all,
stretch across the full spectrum of intellectual achievement.
(And if we turn to chess, certainly one of the ultimate tests of
ability, we find more than fifty per cent of the top players in

every country – Russia, America, Britain and so on – are Jewish.)

Accepting Kinsey's finding that more boys who reach puberty early turn to homosexuality than boys who reach puberty late (though, clearly, early puberty is by itself neither a necessary nor sufficient cause), we would, on Greatrex's basis, expect to find most homosexuals as low achievers. Actually the reverse seems to be the case. Many men of outstanding talent and achievement are homosexual.

There is, then, always an enormous danger in drawing far-reaching conclusions from variables considered in isolation – such as age at puberty. Let us take gestation as a further example – the length of time spent by an organism in the womb. Proceeding through the evolutionary table of primates, we find the period of gestation for the animals named to be as follows.

tree shrew	6 weeks
lemur	18 weeks
macaque	24 weeks
gibbon	30 weeks
chimpanzee	34 weeks
man	38 weeks

The increasing length of time spent in gestation correlates very significantly with the intelligence displayed by each of these species as adults. Ergo, the amount of time spent in gestation is a causal factor in the development of intelligence. No. Nergo. For the elephant spends eighteen months in the womb.

The lesson is that individual factors are of significance only in terms of the *total equation* of an organism. They have a conditional value only.

Nor, at all, must we imagine that nature's hands are ever really tied in any respect – she does not *have* to organize organisms in any particular way. Just because there happens to be in a particular case or cases a high correlation between the length of time spent by the offspring in infancy and the intelligence of the adult, does not mean that nature could not arrange matters any other way. What is on view is really just a happenstance. (By contrast, in the purely physical world nothing happens by happenstance. Things there are always the way things have to be.) Science fiction writers, certainly, have made a major contribution by showing how other happenstances might have worked out in other places.

Nevertheless, I think I can show what I mean by happenstance by reference not to science fiction but to actual matters on this planet – where real-life situations sometimes seem to eclipse even the imagination of the S F writer.

In Australia natural forest fires are common. These mainly involve the undergrowth of the forest. The fire moves rapidly through the woodland, scorching but not destroying the larger trees. This periodic stripping away of undergrowth has important ecological consequences for Australian organisms – and it is some of the details of these which are quite daunting. Some trees, for example, will only shed their seeds after a fire, waiting years for this opportunity. For obvious reasons connected with nutrition and competition, the seeds then stand a better chance of healthy growth. In yet other cases the seed, shed normally be the tree, will only germinate after a fire – after the seed has experienced temperatures of several hundred degrees Fahrenheit – has, in fact, been burned.

In the dry deserts of central Australia rain can fall as infrequently as once in a hundred years. When such rain occurs, in the form then of a torrential deluge, the desert is abruptly carpeted with flowers, with butterflies disporting themselves among them, and lakes and rivers jumping with fish and frogs. It seems that the eggs and seeds of these organisms can withstand very extensive periods of total drought. Not only can they stand it – but some will not germinate *unless* they have first been blown about for several decades over the face of the desert.

These circumstances make complete nonsense of any general statement based on observations of European flora, about the conditions necessary for plant growth. The way plants grow in Europe just happens to reflect the conditions those plants need. Actually, it is in fact the wrong way round to say that the plants 'require' certain conditions. It is the conditions which have 'required' the plants.

In short, there are no laws of nature in respect of organisms. There is only the expediency of nature.

I am really on two different tacks at once now. I am saying, on the one hand, that we can understand an organism only by studying simultaneously *all* aspects of its nature – its present structure, its past and present environment and its evolutionary history. I am also saying that we cannot deduce general laws about how life *must* function by the study of the examples to hand. (The recent Mars probes are bidding fair to demonstrate the truth of this view.) The only real lesson so far is that we *do not know* the limits of life's potential adaptability.

Such heady reflections, however, must not distract us from the reality in hand – which is human life on this planet at this point in time. The behaviour and attributes of an existing organism at a point in time are, as I have suggested, the outcome of the total prevailing organism–evolution–environment equation. Behaviour (and intelligence is a behaviour) cannot be other than the total equation permits – or at least, it cannot be *dramatically* other, though perhaps some small room for manoeuvre exists. Greatrex himself seems to have been in no doubt about the rightness of the formula: past environment (evolutionary pressure) leads to present physiology, leads to present behaviour.

'Past environment' is a term which of course requires further division into extra-species environment (natural selection) and intra-species environment (mainly, though not entirely, sexual selection). When we look at the many present differences between men and women, some are clearly attributable to natural selection, others to sexual selection.

An instance of natural selection is the circumstance that the reaction times of females to various stimuli are slower than the reaction times of males, at all ages. It is in the nature of males to expose themselves more to danger than females – by exploring, fighting and tree-climbing as boys, and by fighting and hunting as adults. There is therefore a premium on fast reaction – those who react fastest escape death more often and for longer, so being in a better position to pass on their genetic make-up to the next generation.

The fact that females on average speak earlier than males, speak better than males, show fewer speech defects of all kinds than males and learn foreign languages better than males, appears also to be linked to natural selection rather than to sexual selection. That woman uses language for social rather than intellectual communication is evident from a glance at world literature. The basic purpose of her superior gift is, I suggest, to communicate with the children, and later to assist communication between the adult male and the children. Children, as is well known, require adequate verbal stimulation from birth onward if they are to develop normally and to maximum potential. (Deaf babies require extra stimulation by touch, smell and sight to partly make up this vital lack. A normal baby is secure as long as it can hear its mother's voice – while a deaf baby must see her.)

One further glance at some rather remarkable data, gathered in 1910 but still awaiting explanation. The differences involved seem to me to be inescapably the results of natural selection, though to what end is by no means clear. As far as we know, such differences are found throughout European peoples – but if test results exist for Africans and Asiatics, I have not seen them. Briefly, the results in question show that when asked to make a freely-associated verbal response to a stimulus word, children almost never give a word of opposite sense, but instead extend the attributes of the thing or situation given (Table 1). Adult men, however, very often respond with a word of opposite sense (Table 2) while women produce mixed results mid-way between the two extremes.

Table 1 Extended response to a stimulus word

Stimulus word	Response word	Per 1000 children	Per 1000 women*	Per 1000 men
man	work	168	17	8
soft	pillow	138	53	42
dark	night	421	221	162
table	eat	358	63	40

Table 2 Opposite response to a stimulus word

Stimulus word	Response word	Per 1000 children	Per 1000 women*	Per 1000 men
man	woman	8	394	561
soft	hard	27	365	548
dark	light	38	427	626
table	chair	24	274	333
Average opposite response to the 100 stimulus words		43	298	473

In support of this data, and as Otto Jesperson first formally reported, we find that very young children habitually confuse words of opposite meaning. They say 'down' when they mean 'up', confuse hot and cold, long and short, and so on. They seem to have no sense of oppositeness. Those theorists (myself among them) who support the view that 'ontogeny recapitulates phylogeny' believe that children in the course of growing up briefly repeat the evolutionary history of our species. It would seem therefore that mankind once had no sense of oppositeness. (The legend of Adam and Eve, incidentally, also says this in symbolic form.) This behaviour seems to some extent to be retained by adult females, for reasons which are by no means obvious.

We are, at any rate, allowed to say that in this respect women are more childlike than men. Yet they become adult (= reach puberty) earlier. Certainly, matters are not simple.

A powerful instance of *sexual* selection is woman's constant concern with her appearance. In all primates it is the female who displays, and the male who is attracted by the display. (In birds the case is completely the other way about.) While the presence of a male will certainly cause an increase in display activity, nature is careful to see that the female's interest in her appearance is very largely self-stimulated – and so functions also in the complete absence of the male, for whose especial

* Because of the experimenters' method of reporting results, those for women alone have to be estimated. The figure given however is the most conservative estimate: in fact the women responded even less frequently with the word of opposite sense.

benefit this behaviour is nevertheless designed in evolutionary terms. (So a bird, in captivity, will swoop and catch non-existent insects.)

I once knew a Swedish girl, very intelligent, very independent and contemptuous of woman's alleged role in life. She often made the point that she did not use make-up. I reminded her of the cream she put on her face at night. 'Oh,' she said, '*but everybody* uses skin cream!' Well, that depends on whom you mean by everybody. It is true that around twenty-five million women in Great Britain use it. But equally there are twenty-five million men who do not.

Still more revealing perhaps is the following incident. I was working temporarily in an office, collecting information over the telephone for holiday guides. There were about twelve of us working in the large office, males and females mixed. Every now and again one of the girls would announce that she was going out to the shops – did anyone want anything? Usually there was a chorus of yeses from the girls, though as far as I noticed none of the men ever responded. I never actually heard any girl tell any other what she wanted – but this circumstance never struck me, until one day I found one page of a list on my desk, where it had arrived by accident. Bear in mind, incidentally, that the prices quoted are those of 1974 – and they seem high even now.

W

Tug-boat soap set   58p
New Country Kitchen Powder
Sachet Moonwind   £1 15p
Snowmen 3   1 Moonwind
1 Charisma and 1 Elegance   (48p each)

K

Skin So Soft bath oil and talc   87p

L

Honeysuckle Cream Sachet + talc   79p
1 Snowman   48p

No wonder the girls never had any sandwiches at lunchtime.

On a rather different tack, it never fails to surprise me that psychologists do not ask themselves where, in the human female, the complex monitoring mechanisms that govern the development of the embryo are located. I cannot imagine this process not requiring some very formidable information banks, override circuits and whatever, particularly as pregnancy has such a marked effect on woman's psychology. Perhaps the circuits are located in the ganglia. (Or perhaps, as I usually suggest, in the cerebellum.)

It has at any rate been established that in rats and some other animals a female with the cerebral cortex totally removed still performs sex and maternal acts with very little loss of fineness. A male rat with the cerebral cortex similarly removed, however, cannot perform the sex act at all. Massive doses of additional hormone have no effect. This experimental work, I must emphasize, has not been carried out on primates – and even if it were, we should not necessarily be able to argue straight to human beings. Still, as far as the evidence goes, it does suggest that some human female activities are not primarily located in or monitored by the cerebral cortex.

So is the 'vacant' cortex in females used for some other purpose – or is it perhaps not used at all?

There is a palatial house in Hampstead, London, where in the very corner of a vast, marbled room a little old Jewish man sits at an old desk on a scrap of matting. Fifty or sixty years ago he sat in a tiny hut in Romania, at just such a desk, doing whatever it exactly is he does. Here in London he does not use the rest of his house. It has grown up around him.

I think from many points of view the brain and the nervous system have grown up around us. There are lots of empty rooms in them, not yet used. Sometimes in men and women different rooms are left vacant. There is in fact actually nothing new in the at first surprising suggestion that brain and other neural structures can exist without being used. Neanderthal man had a much larger brain than our own, for example, an average 1400 cc as against our own 1300 cc.

Not just the physiological hardware but the psychological software, it seems, has also grown up around us.

In recent years it has become clear that organisms have a very wide range of fully fledged responses that they are never called upon, nor *have ever* been called upon, to use. These were stumbled upon by accident by ethologists in the course of the experimental investigation of response mechanisms. They concern coloration, sexual attributes, egg size, litter size, nest- and home-building materials, and many other matters.

Human males, for example, respond maximally to an exaggerated and stylized female form that does not exist in nature. This 'model' has the toes fused together, improbably long legs, a tiny snub nose tilted to vanishing point to expose the nostrils, eyelashes half an inch long, and so on.

The response of organisms to form generally seems to exist prior to the existence of the form itself: so that the 'desires' of organisms, in all senses of the term desire, clearly shape the *future* attributes and *evolutionary direction* of a species, in terms both of sexual and of natural selection. I am myself led ultimately to the conclusion that response always exists before stimulus – a complete reversal of the classical Darwinian position.

These, however, are centrifugal speculations, threatening to lead us too far from Greatrex. Back, therefore, to specifics.

My single main objection to the psychologists of the Greatrex school, really, is in their complete neglect of the *autonomic nervous system* as a vehicle of thought or evolved consciousness, instead entirely favouring the cerebro-spinal or central nervous system.

Here, however, is what C. G. Jung had to say about the autonomic nervous system.

It turns out that bees not only tell their comrades by means of a peculiar sort of dance that they have found a feeding-place, but that they also indicate its direction and distance, thus enabling the others to fly to it directly. This kind of message is no different in principle from information conveyed by a human being. In the latter case we would certainly regard such behaviour as a conscious and intentional act ... Thus we are driven to the conclusion that a nervous substrate like the sympathetic system, which is absolutely different from the cerebro-spinal system in point of origin and function, can evidently produce thought and perception just as easily as the latter. What then are we to think of the sympathetic system in vertebrates ?*

My own belief is that logical and intellectual thought is only very highly evolved muscle (the cerebro-spinal/central nervous system); while religious states, intuition and emotion are very highly evolved viscera (the autonomic nervous system).

It is not hard to show that the central nervous system in women is relatively less well developed – the slower reaction times, for instance, and the fact that female muscles cannot do the full work of male muscles. And, conversely, that the auto-nomic nervous sytems of women are more developed than in males. Extremely apropos here, we have the already-mentioned requirements for having a baby, along with the monthly menstrual cycle. It is usually said of course that a woman has a baby, but in fact it is the baby (the blood-sucking embryo) which has the woman – sometimes dictating to her, for instance, what foods she shall eat. As for menstrua-tion, more women commit suicide at that time than at any other, underlining the marked effect which the menstruation process has on conscious mood. We note further that women sleep more than men, blush and cry more easily, and so on. And of course reach puberty earliest of all . . .

These clear indicators at the physiological level are suppor-ted by other indicators at the psychological level. Women dream more than men (both absolutely and relatively), are hypnotized more easily than men, are more suggestible than men, and are more concerned with love than men. Con-versely, as seems abundantly clear, women are not foremost among the world's greatest intellects. Oh, but good heavens, interrupts the environmentalist at this point, what about opportunity?

During the seventeenth and eighteenth centuries middle-class girls and young ladies received a thorough training in composing verse, painting and playing the piano. Usually

*C. G. Jung, *Synchronicity: An A-Causal Connecting Principle* (Routledge & Kegan Paul, London, 1972).

they were individually tutored, or perhaps along with one or two companions. They also had nothing else to do. Yet what original music, painting or verse sprang from these hordes of tutored, intelligent young women? Virtually none. And, further, what of their counterparts who passed their lives in nunneries, reflecting on the nature of God? Where are their books and treatises of philosophy, religious or otherwise – the equivalents of Teilhard, St John of the Cross, Aquinas? Nowhere.

It is not true, you know, that women could not get published. This is a malicious story put about by the Brontës and George Eliot. I have a delightful book, published in 1852, entitled *Anecdotes of the Habits and Instincts of Animals*. The author's name is in bold print on the title page: Mrs R. Lee. The book was evidently a roaring success, for in the following year she published: *Anecdotes of the Habits and Instincts of Birds, Reptiles and Fish*. (I have quoted from these excellent books in my own next book.)

So I personally feel we cannot allow lack of opportunity. Only lack of ability and, importantly also, lack of motivation. If there *was* any prejudice against books by women, I think it probably arose from the circumstance that these *in general* were not very good. Of course, there were notable exceptions.

I think we can (and should) finally quell all the arguments about aptitudes being the outcome of present environmental opportunity (the nature-nurture issue) by reference to our primate cousins. Jane van Lawick Goodall spent some years living with and observing chimpanzees in the wild. She tells us that girl chimpanzees like nothing better than to play with the new babies and to be allowed to nurse and to hold them. (I remember in the working-class district in which I grew up, how the little girls would knock on the doors and ask if they could have the baby for a while.) Boy chimpanzees, meantime, prefer to rampage round the jungle in groups, fighting and exploring. Presumably Jane Goodall cannot be accused of male chauvinism.

Oh but, says our shadow environmentalist, the chimpanzee is so entirely ruled by instinct that choice could never come into it. Not at all. Jane Goodall also tells a moving story about a little girl chimpanzee, Gilka, who for a whole year used to steal away from the troop to play with a little girl baboon, Goblina, who likewise absented herself from her baboon group. Is this not choice behaviour? Shades of Romeo and Juliet – well, almost – right there in the jungle.

It is, in any case, not easy to draw any firm line between choice and instinct in higher animals – in primates especially and man in particular. Instinct always tends to colour choice. Most girls are interested in fashion – and, as it happens, adornment and display form part of their instinctive equipment. Most men enjoy competitive sport and games of one kind or another – and, as it happens, male dominance hierarchies are a regular feature of primate social life.

I am myself moved to ask, who, at this present moment, is stopping girls from crawling about under cars and tinkering with car engines? Surely only girls themselves. Who is forcing men to tinker with engines in their free time? Nobody. It is true that there is a force called social role, which subtly reinforces our inclinations in particular directions. But where do society and social roles themselves come from? These are only the outward expression of what we are in the first place. The kibbutz experiment now described shows clearly the truth of this view.

The kibbutz in question set out to destroy socio-sexual roles. All tasks of all kinds were equally performed by men and women, in rotation. But after twenty-five years, the old traditional roles had reasserted themselves. The women had requested their traditional jobs back.

Present environment (society) can slightly modify the expression of a talent or an inclination. But it can never create talents on the one hand, nor materially prevent their expression on the other. In a time of maximum opportunity a particular woman is Jane Goodall, a trained zoologist in the field and a writer of good books. In a time of less opportunity she is Mrs R. Lee, a writer of good books and a gifted amateur naturalist. (From the mass of crazy animal stories then in circulation – six years before the publication of Darwin's

Origin of Species, remember – Mrs Lee's sure instinct led her to select only those that were true, and which in some cases have been confirmed only by recent observation.)

I am especially impressed with the case of the cuckoo. Reared as a solitary youngster by any of a couple of dozen kinds of foster-bird – and never having so much as seen another cuckoo until itself an adult, it is, nevertheless, a perfect cuckoo with all cuckoo behaviours.

I am also as much gratified as impressed that over the past years many of the trendy psychologists and sociologists I graduated with, having become parents, now tell me shame-facedly, or simply in bewilderment, that the sharply differing personalities of their various children were in evidence from the moment of birth, becoming accentuated with each passing day.

The rose bud unfolds as best it may in the circumstances in which it finds itself. But what unfolds is always a rose, never a hyacinth. The flowering of personality is an essentially similar process.

David Livingstone, of working-class origin, was employed at the age of ten in a cotton mill as a child labourer. He stayed there fourteen years. Nevertheless, he became one of the world's greatest explorers. Christy Brown was born a severe paraplegic in an Irish working-class family. He was left ignored to drool in a corner. Today he is a renowned novelist, typing his work with one big toe on a special machine, at the rate of a couple of words a minute. Graham Hill, the former world motor-racing champion, did not pass his driving test till he was twenty-four. His father could not drive, and never owned a car.

With regard to general intelligence, I think the statements made about personality and specific talents also hold true, if anything more so. Intelligence can be defined as what you do with what you have. Intelligence creates its own opportunities – that, too, is part of intelligence. The only thing that will actually stop a bright child is a bullet. And if a child is not bright, there is almost nothing you can do about it.

Greatrex's suggestion that we effectively breed high

intelligence out of the population by suitably mixed marriages is, unfortunately, a real possibility. However, it would be necessary to make sure that the highly intelligent bred only with the unintelligent. Such misalliances would have to be enforced – requiring Sex Police organized along diametrically opposite lines to those of present South Africa. I am sure the communists would be happy to supply such police. A few years ago in Russia several eminent scientists, who produced evidence that intelligence was genetically inherited, were shot.

So interbreeding might, in a sense, solve the problem of intelligence, ending with us all sitting in the mud picking our noses – but even so, as Ms Kwai observed, 'Operation Brotherhood cannot help women . . .'

In men and women we have not merely differing levels of ability, but two totally different organisms – two different species in fact. And no amount of manipulation of the environment (or sociological twaddle) is going to change that.

Apart from the fact that the task is impossible, I am implacably against the attempt to make women into intellectuals – that is, into central nervous system heavy-weights. They are *autonomic* heavy-weights. So why not rather let them show us what the autonomic system can do.

We know that women dream more than men – and that the large majority of spontaneous paranormal experiences occur in dreams. More women report spontaneous psychic experiences in the waking state than men. More women are mediums than men. And so on. The message is clear. Women are more endowed in respect of the paranormal, and the intuitive generally, than are men. (Logically enough, the autonomic system itself is heavily implicated in paranormal events of many kinds.)

Surely the possession of full paranormal abilities could not and would not be regarded as an inferior endowment to logical, intellectual gifts? Quite on the contrary, I would imagine. Therefore, girls, your task and your duty is clear. You must conquer the paranormal for mankind.

I myself do all I can on behalf of women, and the autonomic system. Just before the commission for this paper landed on my mat I had been typing out a lecture I was giving to the annual conference of the Dartington Society, entitled *Decorticate Cats Still Dream*. (It's true, they do.) The quote at the head of this essay is part of the summary of that lecture for the programme notes.

Synchronistically and otherwise, the two commissions were linked. For my self-appointed task is to break twentieth-century psychology's obsession with the cerebral cortex and the central nervous system. I want the alternative consciousness of the autonomic system to come into its own, to inherit its Promised Land. I want evolved viscera to be seen to be every whit as important as evolved muscle. I want intuition to reign alongside intellect, feeling to be equal with thought.

Further to this end therefore, I am writing this essay specifically for Professor Greatrex up there in – what? – 2015. He is only seventy. Bertrand Russell was still producing at ninety, as was Bernard Shaw. So Greatrex has at least twenty creative years left. My hope is that this essay will be the catalyst to once more speed him along the path on which he has already taken one or two hesitant steps. I now therefore formally urge you, Professor Greatrex. Pull yourself together and try once more – this time, with feeling.

Woe, Blight, and in Heaven, Laughs: a Grim Household Tale

Josephine Saxton

The front doorbell rang. The Writer opened the extremely solid, Victorian, oak door with brass letter-flap and knob, having had to use two keys; one for the Chubb and one for the hinge-bolt, both specially fitted by a Polish expatriate, in his spare time, to keep out furniture burglars. Eight large bullets entered her body at various points, one after the other but so closely spaced in time as to make the interval unsuitable for all but random considerations such as: 'Why me?' She clutched at her white, tailored trouser-suit, horrified at the blood, of a peculiar and almost luminous brilliance which spilled and spilled. She looked to see who had rung the bell, but there was no one. Joke callers again. She looked at her reflection in the hall mirror. She had gone very pale. Her hair looked black in this light (she had closed the door), although in reality it was a dark brown, scorched over with repeated applications of henna: the colour of venison.

'Pull yourself together. You let your imagination run away with you at times.' But how was that to be accomplished? Every five minutes, for almost two weeks, she had been shot down. Several large wounds had torn aside her belly to reveal the usual mess of guts. Always, it was welcome. What was really upsetting was to find herself reasonably alive and well with the exception of tonsillitis, cured by an application of a herbal oil to the swollen neck, a bottle of cheap burgundy and massive doses of vitamin C, she being a follower of Linus Pauling.

'Sick. That's what it is. Sick. You've been bothered by this kind of thing ever since you were little. What's the game?'

151

There had been a history mistress, iron-grey and muscular, dressed in tight, coarse, striped handweave, heavy polished brogues and pink knickers only visible when seated on the desk, expounding about Cromwell whom she so resembled. During history lessons, the Writer who had then been a girl, always had managed to catch a part of herself conjuring an image of herself being lashed over her back with a leather horsewhip of the plaited kind, wielded by the history mistress. Again and again it fell, and with every stroke she felt better in her spirit, her soul, her emotion. She was not bad at history although she was to fail her G.C.E. through spending the evening before the exam being kissed violently by an elderly displaced Pole in the People's Park; she was not in love with the history mistress, she had no lesbian tendencies at all and she abhorred pain as much as any normal animal. It was inexplicable. Seen in retrospect, it was even a source of wonder. It might mean something terrible. That she was repressing evil desires. But, she felt pure. As driven snow. Not purged of all aberration, but never having had any. And therefore, perhaps, a little bit curious.

Woe, Blight, and in Heaven, Laughs by Josephine Saxton

Lucille hated her stepmother. Most people hated Lucille's stepmother, she was a crabby bitch. They were both beautiful, with raven hair, lily-white skin, and scarlet lips and rosy cheeks. Lucille had a slow form of leukaemia, difficult to cure even if there had been proper medical services.

Wholemeal bread was rising in the kitchen. A friend had come to ask her what it was like at the Milford Writers' Conference. Describe it. Ecstatic phrases spring to mind, glowing accounts of useful conversations, helpful inter-critical sessions, eating dinner with several other writers, some of them famous. Walking on a pebbly shore enacting future accounts in biographies of herself as yet unwritten – the kind of thing they do about Shelley and Byron in Italy. Criticism, witticism, schism. Being high all the time on booze, writing and writers.

'It's great. I thrive on the company of other writers. I wished I lived in London, or New York.'

'Crazy. But who wants to live in a plastic city?'

'Who wants to live in a family house, hemmed in, nowhere to go, attacked by dwarfs, eaten up by other's needs, baking bread as the high-spot of the day, lonely, frustrated, etc. etc. etc.'

'Not the liberation theme, *again*?'

'Sorry.' He offered her some mescalin, a late Christmas present. She had not time for days off for such trips: the guerillas and their unseemly attacks came from somewhere else, not from a drugged nightmare.

'How's the writing going?'

'I have just completed a crime novel.'

'Cripes! Selling anything?'

'Some. Not enough. I think I've got to go out and get a job.'

Lucille's father was dead, from repeated overdoses of various drugs of the kind that cause people to think that the world is not in a terrible mess, and had left his second wife, Queenie, and his daughter, his beloved Lucille, without any money. Lucille had added very little to the income; she did not like selling herself. There were very few other jobs for women, and those there were usually had extra night-duties of the kind Lucille wished to avoid. Queenie thought this unwillingness on the part of her stepdaughter snobbish and selfish, which, seen in some lights, it was. Lucille dreamed of a healthy, handsome fellow who would love her. Her most outright fantasies included a beautiful doctor with a miracle cure for her leukaemia.

'You won't have much time to write, then, with the children and all.' They closed in suddenly and had ripped her open before she could reply. In a manner essential to any self-respecting Brazilian movie, she slowly followed her perineal contents to the floor.

'Well, you've got guts, I'll say that.'

Queenie went into her private cubicle and switched on her Frend.

'I'd like to ask a few questions, I need a confidence boost. Who is the loveliest of them all?'

'You are Queenie, of course. For your age, you're marvellous.' Have to get it serviced. What kind of an answer was that? But it was no longer a simple matter, getting things serviced. The whole economic structure was wobbly, people didn't care.

The Writer journeyed off into the interior of a story which needed rewriting, according to advice offered at Milford. Brian Aldiss had made some rather negative comments which she could not precisely recall, but the feeling, that recalling the incident induced in her, was divided into two main reactions, which, verbally, would best be expressed by: 'How right you are, Brian, I bow to your superior experience,' or: 'There could be a day when you will be glad to *attempt* a pastiche on Saxton, too.' She reacted similarly to the comments of James Blish, who had expressed the feeling that he was dead sick and tired of myths and fairy-tales being lightly disguised as SF. 'How I agree with you, how I wish I had been able to produce something totally original,' immediately countered by: 'Shit to you, bighead; just because every one of your books is still in print, you think it's going to prevent writers like me, lately out of print, doing exactly what they wish!'

Somewhere between those two reactionary responses, purely from an uncertain ego and of no real value, there must be a truer, more constructive response. She had written a story about Lucille (for light and purity) and her stepmother Queenie (the Jungian archetype Terrible Mother) and seven mutants in various stages of grotesque plight, who worked Underground, somewhere in the future, growing melons, because Overground, nothing would grow at all. A Damon Runyan kind of parody full of disasters hinted at by the sparse dialogue such as: 'Silly cow.'

'What's a cow, Queenie?' There was an uninformed silence.

Naturally, in a future of the kind dreamed-up in ecology stories, cows would be a forgotten manifestation. Sneezy, the Disney dwarf (for she had based it, naïvely, upon the Disney version) suffering from every type of allergy due to fucked-up body chemistry, and calling it hay-fever and not knowing what hay was. Such things are taken for granted in such stories.

Melons are grown hydroponically and apples – well of course, apples are dreadfully poisonous due to the deposits of sprays and nuclear fallout, as in *Silent Spring* but worse. Magic mirrors are television sets programmed to inform the Queen that the Hunter had given her the heart of a deer, and not Lucille's heart to eat, therefore bringing about the final revengeful apoplexy so terrible in Disney, so archetypal in Grimm. It would seem that even today, body chemistry, unaided by drugs, can produce appalling visions, not necessarily bearing any relation to the true, or even the possible.

But that was not the criticism of the story. Horrid visions of a planet despoiled are commonplace in the world of science fiction. Some of the other writers liked the story and demanded nothing more from it than what they were offered. Christopher Priest, for instance, said that the story made him *grin*. The more he read, the more he grinned. Which was right, for she had meant it to be a funny story. People vary so much in what they grin at. Ken Bulmer's heart was wrung by the poor girl's fate at the end of the story.

The wicked doctor found Lucille in an intensive care unit, the transparent tent making her look unreal. He could not believe what he saw, she was so beautiful. Black hair, skin as white as his overall, and lips as red as blood. She hardly seemed to be breathing, so he checked her record. So, this was the girl that the horrid little mutant who thought he was a doctor had been pestering him about. He pondered, and then slipped inside the tent with her. He undid the tapes of her hospital gown, stroked back the hair from her forehead. Trembling, he touched her lips. There was something in her mouth, and he hooked it out with his little finger. So, she was a suicide. Apple was a fairly common method, but she must not have known that it was necessary to gobble several apples quickly, to die fast.

'Well, beautiful, you can die if you wish, but not before we have had some fun together.' He rummaged through his drug supply and filled three syringes. Two contained mixtures of heroin and hallucinogen, and the third contained digitalis, concentrated vitamins, and enzymes. He gave that and one of the hep jabs to Lucille, and waited. She began to breathe visibly and a flush of colour came to her cheeks. He hoped that she would not vomit. He gave himself a shot, fingers crossed that all would go well. He locked the door of the room.

Lucille saw the most handsome man in the world. He looked at her with love in his eyes. They kissed. Everything took on a coloured glow. He was the doctor that she had always dreamed of, come to save her.

There was wonderful and unearthly music somewhere in the background, almost as if it were coming from inside her own body. She had always known that falling in love would be fantastic, but this was more wonderful and beautiful than she could ever have imagined. Suns rose and trees grew against the white wall, flowers bloomed in her heart and every time he touched her it seemed that her flesh turned into jewelled universes. He lifted her up and they pranced round the room, high on a white horse. He asked her to marry him and she instantly accepted. She was in an ecstasy so great that she thought she would die.

'This is what it feels like,' she thought, 'to live happily ever after.'

The Writer had been quite pleased with that last bit of the story, but had not thought it would impress other writers. She was correct, in most cases. What about ordinary people, then? She tried it upon her class of amateur writers, exhorting them to give it a Milford-ing; to be ruthless, honest, searching and perceptive in their criticism. They were deeply shocked. Two left the class, being too embarrassed to voice their opinions, and the remainder stayed bravely to tell her that they considered the story to be nasty, disgraceful, containing rude words, disgusting, horrific and no longer fit for children. It was a matter of some concern to them that a professional writer should spend time re-interpreting fairy-stories in such a way, and that anyone should be so pessimistic about the future. Should I perhaps see a psychiatrist? Would I like to go for a friendly drink after the class, and talk about 'it'?

'But Grimms' tales are not fit for children anyway. How about the one where they put someone in a closed barrel, drive spikes through it and roll him downhill? Charming, isn't it?' They denied that such things were fact but the printed page showed them in error. They too, had taken the Disney version – and the trees in Snow White still haunt the dreams of elderly men and women. It transpired, over beer, that what they had particularly misliked, was her reference to sex. The Lucille in the story had some frightful experiences; was it necessary to elucidate upon them?

'It will be cool, under the earth. Quiet and calm. Push up daisies, daisies are there to be pushed up, I too am a part of the ecological cycle,' said a weary Hausfrau, kneading bread.

'Shall you go to Milford again, this year?'

'No. Definitely not. Can't afford it. The children need new clothes and I haven't had any sun for years. I need new stimulus. I'm starved of sun, I'm as white as a sheet and I cough up blood. I have to have sun, I'm off to Greece, on the cheap, on the bus it is *very* cheap. I shall sleep on beaches.'

'But Milford is valuable for your career. When you got back last time you were so enthusiastic, you said that it was what you needed – the company of other writers. Proper, informed, professional criticism.'

'It is, it is. But I feel guilty spending all that money on the hotel, and the drink.'

'Drink? Can't you talk without drink?'

'I suppose so.'

'Well you shouldn't.' She screamed, clutched herself, reeled dramatically sideways and fell to the floor, twitching in a scarlet puddle.

'This is a fine time to start playing at *High Noon*.'

'Mummy, the bread smells lovely. When will it be ready?'

'Not long. Not long.'

'You are the best baker in all the world.'

'Thank you. I am the most famous, unknown housewife in the world, too, did you know that? All over the world, they've never heard of me. Just climb off me, all three of you, and I will enter my study, which in years past was called a dining-room, and I will write a story. I am re-writing a re-interpretation of a cartoon version of a collected and written-down version of an ancient fairy-tale which sprang from a myth which came from the collective unconscious of the human race, probably Nordic, and it still isn't fit for children.'

'It's never been fit for children. I'd rather see a James Bond, it doesn't give me nightmares the same.'

'Why?'

'Because it isn't real, and *Snow White* is. Sort of.'

'Right. True. I'm glad you see it that way. Would you like to write a letter to Mary Whitehouse elucidating your views on what is, and what is not, corrupting, as a ten-year-old boy, that is?'

'Yes. What is horribly corrupting is the thought that apples are getting to be nasty, that people would spray them that much in the first place. Not getting the right food' and having the Sunday chicken full of hormones is obscene. What I'd like to see on television is more bare tits, they make me feel happy.'

'I have not been a neglectful mother in vain. The lad is progressing nicely.' Then, the bullets, bursting her asunder again. Guilt, that's what! 'But what in God's name am I supposed to have *done*?'

It was when the Frend went berserk on her that Queenie got out of hand and lost her reason. The machine had told her straight to her face that Lucille was better looking than she was, and that she herself was a crabby, mean, old woman. She did not keep the Frend to tell the truth! She would have Lucille wiped out, once and for all. True, she was dying anyway, but it would take time, maybe as much as a year, and time was short for everyone. She would not do the thing herself, but get Gordy Hunter to do it for her. Gordy liked to kill. He would be ideal.

Not here in the apartment, though. Outside somewhere. Perhaps she could stage a love affair between Lucille and Gordy, and get them to walk out some night? Queenie had some extreme types among her friends, and sometimes they came in useful. Black-market contacts, fences, pushers for aspirin and antibiotics. But this would be the first time she had hired a killer – Hunter would be very pleased. It was exciting . . .

Judith Ann Lawrence told her, at Milford, that the story might possibly suggest another story, of deeper significance. The Writer had already written a story where all the seven characters were aspects of the Self, so might not the seven dwarfs be seen as ...? The Writer was uncertain; she was writing a crime novel. Myth, psychology, all of that stuff, was losing its charm.

'What do you learn at Milford?' her friend asked her.

'I learned all kinds of things. I put my commas in with a shaker, my sentences get too involuted for some tastes. I learned a lot about myself.'

'Do you ever think about anything else? What is it supposed to be – gestalt therapy?'

'No. But it is, too.'

'What did you discover?'

'Nothing new, but it became more real. That I wanted to live by myself in a city and not have been a wife or mother. That I was sick of baking daily bread. Tired of being an unknown provincial writer. That I was so isolated from normal life that every time I was in a group I fell in love with everyone. That I talked a lot of nonsense, about Jungian archetypes which other people neither knew nor cared much about, and that I would never be understood if I went on that way – and that although I had already realized that, and wanted to write more realistic and comprehensible, normal-consciousness-level stuff anyway, I was valued only for my craziness, the fact that I commuted between worlds, and seemed to have a different approach to writing than was usual. As Brian Aldiss remarked: "to her, everything in the universe is relevant to everything else." And of course, it is, isn't it?'

'Certainly it is. How could it be otherwise? The trouble being that chaos is a little hard to handle, especially in the written word.'

'Yeah! Bread's ready!' With whoops of joyous glee, the little people ate the bread which she had baked. She then set about putting the house in order, mending their clothes, and polishing the windows. Tradespeople came to the door selling things, but she thought it unwise to spend money that way.

'Do you no harm to look, my dear.' It was an old gypsy, called Violet, who subsequently stank out the house, and who gave her a sample of petticoat lace. How could she refuse?

She allowed her future to be seen. It was full of money, success, fame, great men, journeys over water.

'Your son will become a surgeon, or something in a white coat. (Probably sell ice-cream from a van.) Your other boy will dance and sing and play music. He'll be a one for the girls. And your daughter, ah, your daughter . . .' The crystal grew clouded. Better not say just a wife and mother or I'll throw you out, you old cow, see if I don't.

My mother ate my heart. She showed me a coffin, and commanded me to lie in it. 'Look, it is prepared for you.' I would not get into the coffin, I refused, and her wrath was terrible to behold. 'You belong to me!' she thundered. But it was not true, for already I belonged to someone else: a ring and a certificate proved it.

'It's time you gave up all this psycho nonsense. It's not logical. It doesn't get you anywhere. Just live! Enjoy!'

'I know. But there are certain things which have to be accomplished. I mean, I have to stop people shooting me up, it's a drag.'

'You aren't sexually frustrated, are you?'

'I thought you didn't pay any heed to symbolism? No, I'm not. But I'm very greedy, I'm not monogamous by nature.'

'Are there any other reasons why you would not want to go back to Milford?'

'Yes. When I got back, it was like being shut up in a coffin. Entombed, enslaved . . .'

'Oh God. Not the liberation theme, *again*?'

Lucille was very upset. She did not want to go back to Queenie, and did not want to get the Hunter into trouble. And she did no want to walk the streets, either.

'So, you'll have to work Underground,' said he. Lucille knew that this was the answer; she was dreading hearing it though. How to get a job there? The man called Gordy Hunter knew people, he would get her a job. Then he would tell Queenie that he had killed her, and all would be well. He would get her an easy job. Not everything was automated in the Underground, because it had been started by people long ago who had declared themselves enemies of technology, but there were gauges to be checked. And then, there would be the question of payment to him. After all, he had saved her life.

Next passage censored by the Man in The Street.

She was given a job in the Underground, in the melon gardens, and a bunk in a room with seven other people. The melons were delicious. A strange dark grey colour, but full of nourishment. Artificial vitamins, to be exact.

'Writers need bondage. They should be chained to their typewriters until they have produced writings worthy of – worthy of –'

'I was home a week before I could bring myself to use the vacuum-cleaner. We had shop bread five days.'

'If I were you, I would examine your conscience for the cause of your guilt. Find out why you keep on getting attacked by guerillas in this unseemly way. It is unhealthy. Of what are you guilty?'

'I felt unable to rewrite my story in a satisfactory manner. It was the same with the history mistress. I could have done much better, in history.'

'That's that then. Easy, isn't it?'

'No. A story is a story is a story.'

'If I were you then, I would relinquish not only all that psychological stuff in your fictions, but your fictions. You should clean your house all day, bake bread without let, make everything by hand, have no red wine, stop rolling those disgusting cigarettes, wear unfashionable clothes, have the telephone taken out so that you are even more lonely and get yourself a glass coffin and lie in it when you are not on call for services of various kinds. How much do you want for your I.B.M.?'

All her friends in the Underground were small, making it easier for the eight of them to live in one room. There was Charley, who was mongoloid. He worked away at his job rhythmically and faultlessly, and did nothing but smile all day. A nicer fellow nowhere, apparently. And Job, who was depressive; he was always miserable, poor man. Lucille at first spent hours trying to cheer him up, taking him onto her lap as if he were a baby, and rocking him, but he always ended-up weeping; he just suffered from permanent melancholia. He told her that he had been born like that, with genetic malfunctioning of his hormones. Then there was John who could hardly keep awake. He had to be hopped-up on various kinds of speed to get through a day's work, and then he sometimes suddenly slept in the middle of a sentence or an action. Congenital narcolepsy. He would have died as a baby but his mother had stuck pins into him to keep him awake while feeding.

Then there was Alvin, who gave the appearance of being moronic. He had a very large head and very short arms, but never did anyone any harm. The others helped him dress because he forgot how to do things, sometimes.

And Carl, very timid and agoraphobic. Even the suggestion of going Overground would bring on such a fit of terror that his friends carefully avoided speaking of such places. And then there was Percy who was very intelligent, and who wanted to be a medical man. He had not been allowed to go to medical school because of his size and shape. He was ideally built for cleaning out drainage tubes on the hydroponic tanks. He knew quite a lot of medical lore, and some of it seemed to work. He obtained drugs, too. He obtained John's speed, vitamins P and B_{12} for Lucille, and various things for Peter's allergies, which were numerous. This other one was piteous, for he had rashes and hives and sneezing attacks and palpitations, and it was silly to call it hay-fever for there had been no hay in his lifetime. Lucille had to get used to being sneezed upon, but in the end she accepted it because he just could not help it, at all. In between orgasmic explosions and scratching, he was a really nice person. She had a good bunch of room-mates. She was lucky.

But would she ever meet the wonderful doctor who would love her and save her life? She thought not. Alas!

'What do you think I am? A masochist? You have settled my question. I shall be going to Milford.'

She picked up the machine-gun and stood behind the door, waiting. The doorbell. She poked the weapon through the letter-flap and let go with a burst. This time, she would get it in first. She opened the door, with much scraping and clanking.

The postman. Oh God in Heaven.

The bloodstained letter was from James Blish. It asked for the story that she had presented at Milford. It did not after all matter if it was not extensively rewritten. One did not *have* to rewrite, one did not *have* to take all the advice given.

'But they were right. It was a terrible story.' She read: 'Though we may have been of no use to you, you were valuable to everyone else. Nobody else then, and in the larger group this time, has anything more than remotely like your approach to writing, and we need anyone who can exemplify that there are nine and sixty ways, of constructing tribal lays, and every single one of them is right.'

'True. They were none of them into myth, much. There were no real Jungians, *per se*. They delved but lightly, on the whole, into the unconscious, collective or otherwise. Surrealism, to them, is Dali. They were not overconcerned with varying concepts of reality, the interconnectedness of all things, or with riding across a desert on a bike, trying to stay balanced because of the poisonous snakes. They were all sane. And they did not have my problems with guerillas.'

She turned the postman over, with her foot. Struck down in the performance of his duty. It was their own fault. Sometimes weeks would go by and there would be no mail, to do with her writing, at all. The tension was too much.

She approached her I.B.M. in her own unique way. With a wooden spoon between her teeth she tapped out:

Queenie, disguised as a saleswoman, rooted around in the suitcase amongst dentures, part-used lipsticks and other useful things, and finally found the apple.

'Oh! But that's an *apple*! Everyone knows that they aren't fit to eat.' She was horrified. Apples were lethal. Full of deposits of insect sprays, fall-out, and heaven knew what else.

'Not that apple, dearie,' lied Queenie. 'How long have you been down here, not to know that they are growing them under glass. It is going to be a successful experiment, although they aren't on sale yet. I got this through a contact.'

The beautiful red colouring was driving Lucille mad with greed. Everything down here was grey. Scarlet and shiny. Looked so good.

Queenie eventually sold the apple; a triumph of salesmanship.

Even as she was deploring her own selfishness in not saving the apple to share with her seven friends, she had bitten into it. By the third mouthful she believed her senses, which told her that it was nasty, but by then, it was too late. Poisons, absorbed through her mucus membranes, effected changes in her brain. The atomic structure of some tranquillizers and some insecticides, for example, are very close.

When she realized that she was paralysed, she still had time to wonder why she had been conned so violently?

She fell as dead, a piece of apple still between her lips.

On the question of rewriting the story, the Writer eventually found herself in one of those situations where the work made sense on several levels, in several ways, and knew that she could not choose one or the other, alone. There was always this parallel, or confusion, between realities. Sometimes a metaphor was merely an explanation. It was irritating, too, when an explanation, an attention call, was taken to be a metaphor . . .

And then the new doctor came around the wards, and looked at Lucille, lying in the oxygen tent.

'Is there really any point in retelling myths and fairy-tales? They always come out the same, basically, don't they?'

'Well, I *suppose* they do!'

'And this is what it feels like,' thought Lucille, 'to live happily ever after.'

The World as Text:
the Post-literate World as
Meta-narrative

Angela Carter

The double narrative of Lucille and Writer (their melded adventures and the mutual illumination the one text throws upon the other) suggests the idea of the explication of the text as a method of investigating the phenomena of the world.

Saxton transforms the domestic, everyday world of Writer into the apocalyptic world of Lucille by a system of verbal transformations within a mythic (i.e. culturally familiar) framework. In this way, she also transforms the world itself into a text – material for examination by means of a specific critical methodology.

Since its inception ('in the beginning' according to some commentators), the word has been used as a vehicle for the communication of ideas, instructions, desires and commands. Since language has been the instrument with which, traditionally, we shaped our world, it is easy to imagine how the world could have been constructed out of words and words only. This is the world of the book, the world of pure text, which Lucille and Writer both perforce inhabit because they are made of words themselves and so have nowhere else to live.

But if the word was in the beginning, it may not necessarily be at the end. Mightn't it be possible to set Lucille and Writer free from the text? Well, not in the form that they have taken on due to the exigencies of text itself.

The limitations of our language are the limitations of our lives; but language is not of necessity verbal. The word itself becomes eroded as the sign of an idea in a world in which ideas may be expressed as themselves, by-passing the mediation of the word through a system of immediately perceived images. The word retreats into its own purity; the tower of Babel, original home of the word, becomes an ivory tower where the word resides in solitary, immaculate isolation.

Yet narrative recorded in a system of notation – any system of notation, from the written word itself to the ideograms of television images – is automatically a linear discussion of the world.

To concretize verbal structures as written word becomes more and more a quaint, nineteenth-century kind of hobby, like pokerwork, and writing itself a William Morris handicraft. Today, even the most sophisticated electric typewriter has something of the air of a piece of industrial archaeology about it – a visible archaism that reveals, in its keyboard and its bank of print, a reservoir of the raw material of the word, its own unbroken descent from the fabrications of Caxton.

The writer, who thought himself so important, who thought he was able to make up new worlds through the manipulation of the old words, is left gasping, with his impotent vocabulary, by the advent of post-literate man and the evolution of a sensibility reared on the interpretation of a continuous stream of visual/aural images that by-pass the word, *as such*, altogether.

They by-pass the word, but they do not by-pass narrative. Every night, the commercial channels transmit to us a stream of randomly-associated mini-narratives in the form of television commercials, narratives that differ from those of regular prose fiction in words on paper, only in that their forms always demand a happy ending, stereotypical as the happy endings of the fairy-tale, a convention from which Saxton so memorably departs.

These narratives, with their modified versions of princes, princesses, millers' sons, ogres, magical apparatuses and seven-league boots, their exiguous verbal content in which the word itself is often reduced to a ritual chant, and their overriding need to transmit to us a message about margarine, cigars or washing-powder shows us how ideas may be communicated with, literally, the speed of light in the form of picture-writing.

We must throw away the books.

We must, alas, throw away the myths and fairy-tales, too, and learn to look freshly at a world without words.

A world that has become a book composed in a new language and we must learn to read it.

We are post-literate Adams in a new creation and must set ourselves to the task of un-naming.

But post-literacy does not mean the end of literature; literature is a form of narrative, that's all, and words are not the bricks of which literature is built. Ideas expressed as images are the bricks from which literature is built.

To change the image – the world is a wood of literature that we are often unable to see because of the trees, the print, the printed words, that get in the way.

It would be possible to make an elaborate exegesis of Saxton's story which uses the forms of literary criticism and textual analysis to suggest a philosophic methodology that sees the world itself as a continuous narrative, or system of narratives, to be construed in the terms of the literature that is the world. Before us lurks the teasing prospect of a post-literary criticism, which will take every aspect of life as its material and will become the ethics of the twenty-first century.

A gesture, a sign or an image can express an idea in the same way as a word does. A post-literate generation will develop a sensibility based on reading the language of signs. They will seem to fly from notion to notion, like birds, leaving no trace of their airy passage behind them, whereas we word-bound, print-blinded literate ones have been creeping like snails, exuding in our wakes a long, slimy track of writing to mark our strenuous passage.

The volatile and allusive narratives of post-literacy will need a critical faculty to explicate them, of a type we cannot imagine yet, because, although the image may not be tied to a word, we still identify the image by a word. We would immediately identify Saxton's dwarfs, even if she did not do it for us herself, by the words Walt Disney used to name, or describe, his images of dwarfs – Sneezy, Dopey, Grumpy etc.; nevertheless, we would have recognized them on sight, had we only been able to see them, and not needed to lassoo them with a word.

A new syntax for a visual grammar will form itself to give a formal structure to the post-literate vocabulary. As the world itself is, more and more, seen to be pure literature, a gush of literature like a gush of crude oil, then we will grow used to the idea of interpreting everything around us in the terms of continuous, intersecting narratives beneath the surface of which may be seen sets of pre-existent, partially-eroded, yet still significant, other narratives – as they may be seen to exist here, in the palimpsest of Saxton's tale; yet, since the tale still has words adhering to it, we see the world through it, as in a glass, darkly.

As we accustom ourselves to a world in which 'literature' is no longer either a read or a written thing, but an experienced thing, the word itself will founder under the idea it represents.

Then Lucille and Writer will emerge from the prison of the text and engage us as equals.

Introduction by Professor David Smith
to H. G. Wells 'Foretelling the Future'

Although H. G. Wells is regarded as the main father of science fiction – scientific romances, he called his stories – and he continued to write in that vein until fairly late in life, he never really discussed the technique of his writing. A few brief sentences in his *Autobiography* are all we have had until recently of the Master's views.

Wells was invited to Australia in January 1939 to give an important address to the Australian–New Zealand Association for the Advancement of Science. As he was one of the very few British literary figures ever to tour Australia, he was lionized by the population. Eventually, his sharp comments on Munich, his predictions of a war soon to come, with the possibility of a Japanese invasion, and his caustic remarks on censorship, the White Australian policy and the support of the Australian Prime Minister for appeasement, caused many Australians to be happy to see him leave at the end of his five weeks' visit.

Rank and file Aussies remained entranced, however. Their support was so great that the Australian Broadcasting Corporation asked H.G. to give several lectures. One he entitled 'Fiction of the Future'. In the broadcast he discussed some of the problems he and any science fiction writer faced. In the talk he also discussed some of the difficulties encountered in the Korda–Wells classic film, *Things to Come*. Wells had recently published 'Star-Begotten', and he had just read the proofs of 'The Holy Terror'.

The text of Wells's talk was reprinted in several Australian newspapers. The one we print is taken from the *Adelaide Advertiser*, 30 December 1938, and the *Melbourne Leader* of 7 January 1939, which have the best texts, although nearly all the Australian newspapers printed at least part of the speech, which Wells had read from Perth on 29 December 1938 over the stations of the Australian Broadcasting Corporation. A copy is in the H. G. Wells Archives at the University of Illinois, but the text given here seems to be the speech as Wells gave it – the considered view of the founder on How Best To Do It and The Pitfalls To Be Overcome. And even a plot line to try if one so chose.

Foretelling the Future

H. G. Wells

It has occurred to me that you might be interested in a few things I have learned about one particular sort of book-writing in which I have had some sort of experience. This is fiction about the future. Almost my first published book was *The Time Machine*, which went millions of years ahead, and since then I have made repeated excursions into unknown periods. Just before leaving England I was finishing the proofs of a book about the last of the dictators, which, you probably will be glad to hear, is due to wind up about twenty-five years from now.

There is something topical about all these prophetic books. The more you go ahead, the more you seem to get entangled with the burning questions of your own times. You may cast your tale a century or so ahead, and even then something may happen next week which might knock your most plausible reasoning crooked.

For instance, who ever thought in 1900 of mankind burrowing underground to escape air raids. In a book in 1898 I put all my population in vast towering cities, and I left the countryside outside. What young man trying to write a story would dare to do that in face of the bomber aeroplane? When I wrote 'Anticipations' in 1900 I was already receding from the idea of those crowded cities, and by the time I wrote 'The War in the Air' in 1908, and 'The World Set Free' in 1914, I had completely reversed that concentration. You might almost think that there was something malicious about the future – as though it did not like to be prophesied about. I thought that anyhow I was pretty safe to take my 'Time Machine' some millions of years ahead and see the Sun cooled down to a red ball and the Earth dried up and freezing.

That is what science made of the outlook in 1893, but since

then all sorts of mitigating circumstances have arisen, and there is no reason to lead us to suppose that there will not be humanity, or the descendants of humanity, living in comfort and sunshine on this planet for millions of years so long as they do not blow it to pieces in some great war climax.

As soon as it has no permanent quality, I should be disposed to class all this futurist stuff as journalism less ephemeral than news in the daily papers. We read and discuss it in our own time, because for the time being it has a bearing on our own problems, and is interesting. If posterity reads it at all, it probably will be to marvel at our want of knowledge and imagination. No doubt our own posterity will write their own futurist stories, and no doubt they will be just as transitory as ours.

I think the best sort of futurist story should be one that sets out to give you an illusion of reality. It should produce the effect of an historical novel the other way round. It ought to read like fact, but alas, do any of us futuristic writers ever get sight of that? None of us has produced anything like it. No reader has ever lived in the futurist novel as he may have lived in the London of Dickens's *Barnaby Rudge*, the Paris of Dumas's *Notre Dame*, or the Russia of Tolstoy's *War and Peace*. The futurist writer has at most the barest germ of things to come, and all your prejudices he has to surmount. He has to throw himself on your willingness to believe. You have to help him. He invites you to embark with him upon collaboration in make-believe, or everything fails. If the writer's imagination gives out, he ceases to feel that you can possibly believe in him, and then he strives to make you believe that all along he was only making fun, and was being sarcastic. That is the case in the extremely dismal picture of Mr Aldous Huxley's *Brave New World*. It became at last a bitter pretence.

A lot of fiction about the future starts as a joke from the outside and does not pretend to be anything more. There is a shock of laughter in nearly every new discovery. Every new discovery is necessarily strange to begin with, and if the writer keeps to that line he will save himself a lot of trouble. Here is an idea from which it would be possible to produce a comic futuristic story, and yet it is a feasible and extra-ordinarily strange and terrifying thing to contemplate. Suppose it is within the range of biological possibility that a means were discovered of producing children, and feminine children only, without actual fathers. Most biologists and doctors would tell you that this is at least a conceivable thing. Do not ask yourselves whether this is possible, do not probe into the amusing problems of individual or mass psychology that it would produce, just suppose this were possible. Then you would have the possibility of a comic, maleless world. You must ignore the fact that it would change the resultant human being into a creature mentally and psychologically different from ourselves. You must carry over every current jibe on womanhood – those referring to the throwing of stones, not keeping secrets, and the use of lipstick and vanity bags.

Suppose now you try to complicate things by carrying out your hypothesis, by endeavouring to imagine how such a possibility would actually work. Psychologists should never speculate on how a girl grew up to womanhood in a manless world. What sort of emotional releases would she discover? How would women tackle the complicated mechanisms of life and government? Would they care less for beauty than they do now, or more, and so on? You would have then to write a far more careful story. You would giggle less, but would find much more interest and complication. It would probably lose itself in dissertations and unrealities, but would be a much finer thing if you could bring it off. Suppose humanity refused to accept that great change. Then you would get nearer still to living possibility. You would probably have to narrow the story down to a small group of people, and would have to see the rest of the world, as it were, out of a window. You would then have a futuristic novel, the highest form of futurist literature.

In spite of my constant preoccupation with the future, I can never satisfy myself with the first chapter. All I have written is romance, and pseudo histories, or anticipations. You can write of mighty embankments, of buildings thousands of feet high, of stupendous aeroplanes. That pays most in the written word, but not when your illustrator gets to work. Directly you come down to real persons seen close up, you meet what is the final and conclusive defeat of futurist imagination – that is, the small material details. That was brought home to me when we made a film called *Things to Come*. It is easy to write of a dictator splendidly clothed, seated at the head of his council, and then go on with the speeches, but when it comes to screening and showing him, you have to see him from tip to toe. How is he going to dress his hair? Will he be clean shaven? We consulted a number of hairdressers, but none of them had any clear idea on the hairdressing in 2035. What sort of clothes would he wear? We invoked the aid of dress designers by the thousand. More new dress materials have been introduced into the world in the last thirty years than in the previous 3000 years, and still the novelties come. We could not even decide whether his garments would be held together by buttons or buckles or zips or safety pins. In my lifetime I have seen the practical disappearance of pins, hooks and eyes. Probably no man under forty today ever had to hook up his wife's dress from behind.

Would our dictator sit down at a wooden table on a wooden chair? All we could think of was slightly modernistic metal chairs and a glass table. We could never get beyond contemporary modernism. That film began with an intense realism. At the end of the film we culminated in a sense of the extremest retailed improbability. We had been trying to anticipate inventions and discoveries, frocks and fancies of scores of millions of our descendants. All that we discovered was that we could not even make it plausible. We realized something else. Suppose one of us or all of us had had a real prophetic vision of the buildings, rooms and garments of 100 years hence. Suppose we had actually put that on the screen. Would anybody have believed it? Would it have been even as convincing as the stuff we contrived?

There you have the reason why no sensible writer who believes in writing for posterity, whether ephemeral or amusing, should follow the vocation of prophecy upon which I have spent so much of my time.

More About Penguins
and Pelicans

Penguinews, which appears every month, contains details of all the new books issued by Penguins as they are published. From time to time it is supplemented by *Penguins in Print*, which is our complete list of almost 5,000 titles.

A specimen copy of *Penguinews* will be sent to you free on request. Please write to Dept EP, Penguin Books Ltd, Harmondsworth, Middlesex, for your copy.

In the U.S.A.: For a complete list of books available from Penguins in the United States write to Dept CS, Penguin Books, 625 Madison Avenue, New York, New York 10022.

In Canada: For a complete list of books available from Penguins in Canada write to Penguin Books Canada Ltd, 2801 John Street, Markham, Ontario L3R 1B4.